Practical Attribute and Variable Measurement Systems Analysis (MSA)

Also available from ASQ Quality Press:

Practical Engineering, Process, and Reliability Statistics
Mark Allen Durivage

The Certified Pharmaceutical GMP Professional Handbook
FDC Division and Mark Allen Durivage, editor

Reliability Data Analysis with Excel and Minitab
Kenneth S. Stephens

Product Safety Excellence: The Seven Elements Essential for Product Liability Prevention
Timothy A. Pine

The Metrology Handbook, Second Edition
Jay L. Bucher, editor

The Certified Quality Engineer Handbook, Third Edition
Connie M. Borror, editor

The Certified Six Sigma Green Belt Handbook, Second Edition
Roderick A. Munro, Govindarajan Ramu, and Daniel J. Zrymiak

The Certified Six Sigma Black Belt Handbook, Second Edition
T. M. Kubiak and Donald W. Benbow

The Certified Reliability Engineer Handbook, Second Edition
Donald W. Benbow and Hugh W. Broome

The Certified Quality Inspector Handbook, Second Edition
H. Fred Walker, Ahmad K. Elshennawy, Bhisham C. Gupta, and Mary McShane Vaughn

The Certified Quality Technician Handbook, Second Edition
H. Fred Walker, Donald W. Benbow, and Ahmad K. Elshennawy

HALT, HASS, and HASA Explained: Accelerated Reliability Techniques, Revised Edition
Harry W. McLean

Failure Mode and Effect Analysis: FMEA from Theory to Execution, Second Edition
D. H. Stamatis

To request a complimentary catalog of ASQ Quality Press publications,
call 800-248-1946, or visit our website at http://www.asq.org/quality-press.

Practical Attribute and Variable Measurement Systems Analysis (MSA)

A Guide for Conducting Gage R&R
Studies and Test Method Validations

Mark Allen Durivage

ASQ Quality Press
Milwaukee, Wisconsin

American Society for Quality, Quality Press, Milwaukee 53203
© 2016 by ASQ
All rights reserved. Published 2015
Printed in the United States of America
21 20 19 18   5 4 3 2

Library of Congress Cataloging-in-Publication Data

Durivage, Mark Allen.
  Practical attribute and variable measurement systems analysis (MSA) : a guide for
conducting gage R&R studies and test method validations / Mark Allen Durivage.
    pages cm
  Includes bibliographical references and index.
  ISBN 978-0-87389-915-4 (hard cover : alk. paper)
  1. Acceptance sampling. 2. Quality control—Statistical methods. 3. Measurement.
I. Title.

TS156.4.D87 2015
658.4'013—dc23   2015021647

ISBN: 978-0-87389-915-4

Publisher: Lynelle Korte
Acquisitions Editor: Matt T. Meinholz
Project Editor: Paul Daniel O'Mara
Production Administrator: Randall Benson

ASQ Mission: The American Society for Quality advances individual, organizational, and
community excellence worldwide through learning, quality improvement, and knowledge
exchange.

Attention Bookstores, Wholesalers, Schools, and Corporations: ASQ Quality Press books,
video, audio, and software are available at quantity discounts with bulk purchases for
business, educational, or instructional use. For information, please contact ASQ Quality Press
at 800-248-1946, or write to ASQ Quality Press, P.O. Box 3005, Milwaukee, WI 53201-3005.

To place orders or to request ASQ membership information, call 800-248-1946. Visit our
website at http://www.asq.org/quality-press.

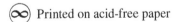 Printed on acid-free paper

Quality Press
600 N. Plankinton Ave.
Milwaukee, WI 53203-2914
E-mail: authors@asq.org

ASQ®   **The Global Voice of Quality**™

Table of Contents

List of Figures and Tables

Preface

This book—a result of 30 years of quality-related work experience—was written to aid quality technicians and engineers. To that end, the intent of this book is to provide the quality professional working in virtually any industry a quick, convenient, and comprehensive guide to properly conducting measurement systems analysis (MSA).

The purpose of this book is to provide background and examples on the application of gage R&R methodology (test method validation) for variable and attribute data, help for those who work with devices that don't fit the usual approach, and ideas for measurement devices that require innovation to assess their performance under off-line, static conditions. The ultimate objective is to ensure the measurement system is suitable for its intended purpose and capable of consistently providing valid measurements so that one may effectively control and ultimately improve the performance of a process. The reader is assumed to be familiar with basic control charting methodology since assessment of statistical control of the measurement process is important.

One may wonder why performing a gage R&R is so important; the simple answers are profit, public health, and safety. Companies that are shipping product that is out of specification can be subjected to expensive litigation, especially in the aviation, pharmaceutical, and medical device industries.

It is the author's contention that decision making on and evaluation of measurement systems should be done in the context of a systems approach. The particular criterion used for measurement capability is less important than the full context of measurement and process variation.

This book will be a useful reference when preparing for and taking many of the ASQ quality certification examinations, including the Certified Quality Technician (CQT), Certified Calibration Technician (CCT), Certified Quality Inspector (CQI), Certified Six Sigma Green Belt (CSSGB), Certified Quality Engineer (CQE), Certified Six Sigma Black Belt (CSSBB), and Certified Reliability Engineer (CRE).

Acknowledgments

I would like to acknowledge the previous work of Larry B. Barrentine in *Concepts for R&R Studies*. This book is an expansion of his efforts and an attempt to continue his style of presenting R&R studies in a simple, easy-to-follow style. I would like to thank those who have inspired, taught, and trained me throughout my academic and professional career. I also wish to recognize my friend, colleague, author of *Implementing ISO/IEC 17024:2005*, and fellow ASQ Fellow Bhavan "Bob" Mehta, principal consultant at GMP & ISO Expert Services, for lending his expertise in reviewing this book for accuracy and content. ASQ's reviewers T. Gourishankar and Autumn Farrell also provided invaluable insight and detailed feedback. A special thanks to my friend and colleague Joshua Dall for lending his expertise and experience in developing the sample study procedure and sample audit checklist included in the appendixes. Additionally, I would like to thank ASQ Quality Press, especially Matt Meinholz, Acquisitions Editor, and Paul O'Mara, Managing Editor, for their expertise and technical competence, which made this project a reality. Lastly, I would like to acknowledge the patience of my wife Dawn and my sons Jack and Sam, who allowed me time to research and write *Practical Attribute and Variable Measurement Systems Analysis (MSA): A Guide for Conducting Gage R&R Studies and Test Method Evaluations*.

LIMIT OF LIABILITY/DISCLAIMER OF WARRANTY

1
Introduction

Gage R&R—repeatability and reproducibility—studies analyze the variation of measurements of a gage (repeatability) and the variation of measurements by operators (reproducibility). Gage R&R studies are also referred to as *test method validation* (TMV) in the Food and Drug Administration (FDA)–regulated industries. To understand why this is so important, recall that the goal of process control is reduction of variation in the process and, ultimately, the product. To address actual process variability, the variation due to the measurement system must be identified and separated from that of the process. Studies of measurement variation are a waste of time and money unless they lead to action to reduce process variation and improve process control. Since you can not address something that can not be measured precisely, the assessment of the gage becomes an early priority during the design and development and transfer phases prior to commercial production.

Before we can continue discussing gage R&R, we have to define "gage." The term *gage* actually refers to any device used for making measurements. In this book, the terms *gage* and *device* are used interchangeably and refer to any device or equipment for making a measurement.

Every observation of a process contains both actual process variation and measurement variation (Figure 1.1). In the case of measurement systems, the sources are:

1. The gage/device.

   a. Calibration—is the gage accurate?

   b. Stability—does the gage change over time?

2. The operator—does the operator have the necessary skill and training?

3. Within-sample variation—variation within a sample is a part of process variation that is often mixed with measurement variation.

4. Repeatability—the variation observed when an operator measures the same sample using the same gage several times.

5. Reproducibility—the additional variation observed when several operators use the same gage to measure the same sample.

6. Linearity—is the gage more accurate at low values than at high values, or vice versa?

7. Bias—is there a shift of the average measurements from the reference value?

8. Discrimination—is the gage sensitive enough to measure the part?

Gage R&R studies assess reproducibility (operator variation) and repeatability (gage variation). *Repeatability* is the variation observed when an operator measures the same sample using the same gage several times (see Figure 1.2).

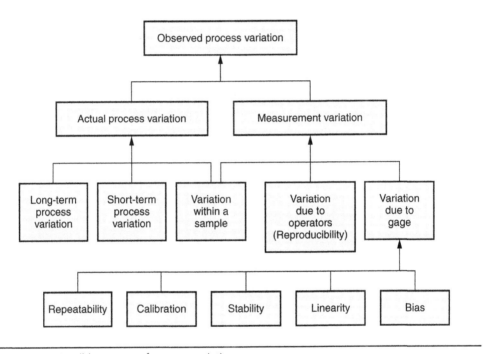

Figure 1.1   Possible sources of process variation.

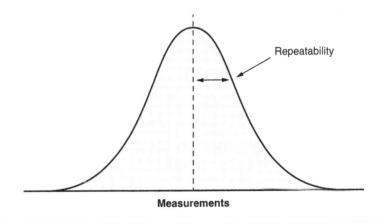

Figure 1.2   Repeatability.

Reproducibility is the additional variation observed when several operators use the same gage to measure the same sample (see Figure 1.3). The combination of both sources of variation is referred to as gage R&R (see Figure 1.4). Note that gage R&R does not address the total measurement system but is narrowly defined and is gage specific.

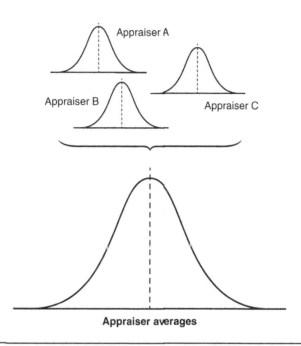

Figure 1.3   Reproducibility.

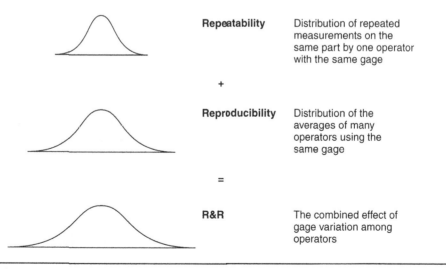

Figure 1.4   Repeatability, reproducibility, and R&R.

The exclusion of the other potential sources of measurement variation does not imply that calibration, stability, or linearity are unimportant; it is just that those sources are ordinarily less significant in their impact. For that reason, gage R&R are often studied and quantified first. In order to improve them, you must address the key measurement process variables via procedures, standards, training, and appropriate studies. We plan and execute gage R&R studies in a fashion designed to avoid confusion with sources of variation other than repeatability (gage) and reproducibility (operator). While this manual describes how to perform gage R&R studies, you can not ignore the other sources of variation for long. In particular, the actual process variation is the ultimate subject to be addressed. Customers require both gage R&R studies and process capability. Process capability includes both process variation and measurement variation. Consequently, gage R&R studies should be accompanied or quickly followed by evaluations of calibration, variation within the sample, and any other relevant source of variability.

Variation within the sample being measured is often difficult to exclude from the gage R&R study. While not attributable to measurement, this source is extremely important and should always be pursued with diligence. It not only has relevance to understanding gage R&Rs but also provides vital information on how to gain process capability improvements.

A specific example of variation within the sample is apparent in measurements of surface texture by a profilometer. The test piece itself is sufficiently variable that if the measurement is made at a random position, the variation within the sample will inflate the estimate of repeatability. It is necessary to identify and measure this variability within the sample; but this alone is not identified by a gage R&R study. The key point is to make certain that process variability within the sample does not intrude on the gage R&R study if it can, or must, be avoided. Determination of an unsatisfactory gage R&R should always lead to an evaluation of whether variation within the sample is part of the problem.

The impact of any environmental conditions also needs to be evaluated. This is more appropriately addressed by designed experiments. Prior to conducting gage R&R studies, an effort is made to block out such sources of variation during the development phase.

It is necessary to introduce the mathematical version of Figure 1.4 since this relationship is used repeatedly. To add distributions, one must add the variances, or σ^2s, of the distributions being added. If the distributions, or spread, due to repeatability and reproducibility can be characterized by their respective sigmas ($\sigma_{Repeatability}$ and $\sigma_{Reproducibility}$), then combining these distributions as in Figure 1.2 results in the following distribution for gage R&R:

$$\sigma^2_{R\&R} = \sigma^2_{Repeatability} + \sigma^2_{Reproducibility}$$

The sigma for gage R&R is the square root of this expression. This same Pythagorean relationship will be used to relate the process variation to the measurement system variation and the part variation (see Figure 1.5).

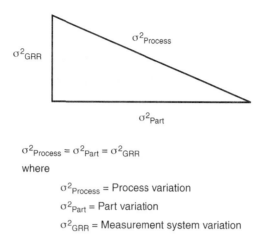

$$\sigma^2_{Process} = \sigma^2_{Part} = \sigma^2_{GRR}$$

where

$\sigma^2_{Process}$ = Process variation

σ^2_{Part} = Part variation

σ^2_{GRR} = Measurement system variation

Figure 1.5   Measurement system Pythagorean relationship.

Throughout this book there are several examples that are fully worked out using a simple scientific calculator. If the examples are worked using a spreadsheet or a commercially available software package, the results can and will vary. The differences are attributed to rounding errors. Although there are differences, essentially the same results and conclusions will be obtained.

2

The Gage R&R Study Life Cycle

The gage R&R study life cycle begins with planning, which is the most important part of conducting a gage R&R study and occurs prior to making any measurements. Ensure that the gage or measuring system is appropriate to the feature being measured or evaluated. During the planning phase, the decisions made or ignored will determine the validity of the study (see Figure 2.1). The plan should be documented in a written protocol and should consider the following:

1. *Determine whether the feature to be measured is an attribute or a variable measurement.* This decision will have a significant impact on the amount of information the system will yield and the number of samples required to conduct the study. Variable data

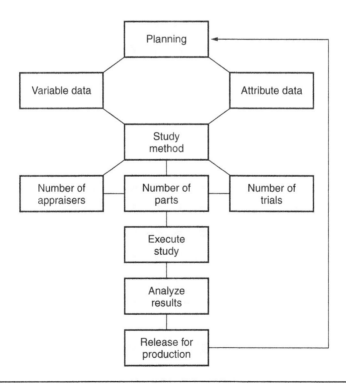

Figure 2.1 Gage R&R study life cycle considerations.

7

provide more statistical information than attribute data. It is therefore recommended, if possible, to use variable data.

2. *Ensure that the device be calibrated and zeroed* (as in the case of a balance or scale). Calibration can affect the gage R&R study. Ideally, the device should be calibrated before the study begins and not recalibrated until the study has ended. If this is not possible, variation due to calibration may appear in the study. Any indication of significant variation due to calibration requires correction:

- If it is necessary to recalibrate after each measurement, then repeatability and calibration variability are combined.

- If each operator must recalibrate before each trial (set of sample tests), repeatability and calibration variation are combined.

- Sometimes, scheduling of operators requires each operator to run all of their trials consecutively; that is, operator A runs trial 1 in random order, then immediately runs trial 2 in a different random order, and so on. In such cases, if each operator only calibrates before beginning, calibration variation will be combined with reproducibility.

- Ensure that the discrimination/resolution of the measuring device is 10% of the total tolerance. For example, if the part feature is 1.000" ±.001, the discrimination/resolution should be 0.002/10 = 0.0002". The measuring device should have a resolution of 0.0002" or better.

3. *Determine the number of appraisers/operators.* Give careful thought to the population represented by the operator(s). Some devices do not have an operator—for example, automatic gages. Treat such cases as if there were a single operator. If a single operator performs all the measurements with the subject gage, then one can not determine an operator effect, and there should be no attempt to create one artificially. Where multiple operators do use such gages, the minimum number required in the study is two. For greater confidence in the estimates, the recommended number of operators in the study would be either three or four, if at least that many are in the operator population. The recommended number is three. Using more than that number is statistically sound but generally makes the study too cumbersome. When a representative sample of operators is to be used in the study, they should be selected randomly. Ongoing studies are planned to eventually cover all appraisers.

Appraisers must be proficient at their task; the operators should have equivalent skill levels. Never have new or poorly trained operators mixed into the study with skilled appraisers. The intent is to assess skilled operators. Problems of differing proficiencies will be apparent when examining the ranges. The training and experience of the operators should be documented.

4. *Determine the number of samples.* If practical, use 10 samples. However, select enough samples so that (# of samples) × (# of operators) is greater than 15. If this is not possible or practical, increase the number of trials (see Table 4.1 for further guidance).

5. *Determine the sample selection strategy.* Parts or samples should cover the range of measurements expected. If necessary, break a measurement variable into homogeneous groupings within which the variability should be consistent and independent of the differences in samples. For example, the precision of chemistry measurements for low-carbon steel may differ from that of high-carbon. It may be necessary to form at least two groups of carbon ranges for study. Each such category should be the subject of a separate gage R&R study. Such categories can usually be identified by noting changes in the specified tolerances (for example, gage ranges, voltage ranges, and so on).

Note that the samples do not represent the process and are not intended to. Since it is not feasible to represent the process with such a small set of samples, it is better to represent the measurement range. This means that the sample variation should not be used in the assessment procedures.

Discreetly and uniquely label each part. The appraisers should be prevented from knowing which part is being measured during the study to ensure that the system is being adequately challenged.

6. *Determine how many trials should be run.* A trial is one measurement on all the samples by each operator. The number of samples and operators in the study determines the minimum number of trials. Two trials are the minimum to calculate a range and are usually sufficient. However, three or more are typically used to ensure there are sufficient data available (see Table 4.1 for further guidance).

7. *Minimize variation within the sample in the gage R&R study.* Studies of some devices may not be able to exclude within-sample variation from the measure of repeatability. In the case of destructive tests, it is often possible to minimize within-sample effects by selecting test pieces from each sample. For example, a texture measurement with a profilometer may require directing the operators to test at exactly the same point, as long as the test doesn't change the characteristic being measured.

If you believe variation within the sample has intruded or will intrude on the study, define special studies to estimate that component of variation. This may not always be possible; if not, at least identify this source as a contributor to the gage R&R assessment.

Presence of variation within the sample will force two gage R&R studies to be run. The order is determined by what is known:

- If you know or strongly suspect variation is present within the sample, run the study on special standards first to avoid such variation, and follow up with a study using production samples.

- Otherwise, run the first study on production samples; follow up suspicious or unsatisfactory results with a study using special samples.

8. Define the environmental conditions for the study. Consideration should be given to temperature, humidity, lighting, and so on, to ensure that the appraisers are conducting the study under the same conditions. Additionally, establish vision standards for the appraisers.

9. *Measurement considerations.* Generate the measurement in the same manner that it is produced in the standard operating procedure for product evaluation. If a single measurement typically is used, then do that in the gage R&R study. If more than one measurement is made and averaged for the official measurement, then do that for the gage R&R. Ensure that all operators report the measurement consistently the same way. Where averages are reported, also record the individual measurements.

10. *Analyzing the results.* The easiest approach to analysis is to plot the sample averages for each appraiser. This approach is easy and statistically adequate. The calculations are easily done. The measurement capability indices should not use the sample variation. Poor results should prompt a careful manual review of the data and results. A graphical technique for evaluating the results is to make a control chart of the ranges of the trials for each operator–sample combination. Plot by operator and interpret as you would any other range chart.

11. *Parts with one-sided tolerances.* Some specifications have a one-sided tolerance. In such cases, it is not possible to do the tolerance analysis (MCI_2). There are two possible alternatives to apply with one-sided specifications:

- Use MCI_1, using the process variation.

- Use an appropriate internal two-sided spec to calculate the tolerance, and then use MCI_2. Document such a criterion and explain its origin.

(See Chapter 8 for definition and discussion of the measurement capability indexes.)

A common error when only an upper spec is given is to assume that the lower spec is zero. While this may be meaningful in some cases, do not use this approach unless it is considered "reasonable" for that application.

12. *Assess the adequacy of the measurement discrimination.* "Measurement discrimination" is the ability to measure small differences reliably. If the round-off in measurement exceeds the actual measurement variation (repeatability), artificially low estimates of measurement variation (repeatability) will result. For example, if a chemical analysis is reported to the nearest hundredth, and the σ of repeatability is less than .01, then the round-off error may be larger than the measurement variation. Calculation of the ranges of repeated measurements will contain a lot of zeros. This forces the estimate of the measurement variation to be lower than it actually is, making the results look better than they are.

Wheeler (2006) provides two rules to determine whether there is a problem of discrimination:

- The ranges calculated on the gage R&R form have three or fewer possible values less than the upper control limit.

- More than 25 percent of the ranges are zero.

If either of these situations occurs, the measurement discrimination is inadequate, and the estimates generated are suspect (probably as an understatement of repeatability).

13. *What can be done about inadequate measurement discrimination?* Only three options are available:

- Measure and report to as many decimal places as the measurement device permits. Limit calculations, however, to one decimal place more than the measured values.

- Seek a better measurement device, one that can measure smaller units.

- If there is nothing else to be done in the near term, you must live with it. Be sure to note that this situation exists. Its impact depends on the process capability of the variable being measured.

14. *Can a gage R&R study ever include more than one gage?* Normally, a gage R&R study is gage specific; that is, each individual device requires its own gage R&R study. Some device types, such as micrometers, have a very large number of units to be evaluated. For such cases, a shortcut procedure is described under "Micrometers" in Chapter 11 that reduces the amount of testing.

15. *Identifying problems that create special causes in a gage R&R study.* To help identify special causes, keep detailed notes surrounding the circumstances and details of the study. Detail the conditions and note any uncontrolled factors that may reasonably be considered to distort results.

16. *One last consideration is the frequency of reexecuting the gage R&R study.* The frequency depends on several factors, including but not limited to:

- A change in the gage

- A change in the specification/feature

- An increase in the amount of rejected product

- An increase in customer complaints

- The effect of the feature on health and/or safety

- A new application for the gage

3

How to Address Variation within a Sample

In some measurement situations, within-sample variation can not be prevented from affecting the gage R&R study, for example, the measurement of roundness of a bar. There is variability in this measurement depending on where the measurement is made on the sample bar. Another example is surface roughness measurements, which may vary significantly across the piece being measured. A third example is a destructive measurement where the same test can not be repeated, such as a tensile test.

The within-sample variation is extremely important and can be a major component of process variation. To understand the measurement variation and the process variation, within-sample variation must be examined. To examine within-sample variation, certain concerns must be addressed in the following order:

1. Have a calibration procedure in place

2. Define the measurement capability excluding variation within the sample

3. Define the variation within the sample

4. Move on to process control

CASE A: EITHER WE DO NOT KNOW WHAT TO EXPECT OR IT IS LOGICAL TO ASSUME NO SIGNIFICANT VARIATION WITHIN THE SAMPLE

In such instances, perform a gage R&R in the routine fashion, making no effort to avoid the effect of variation within the sample. This would mean that you would not tell the operator to test or retest at the same location:

1. If the gage R&R calculations for repeatability are satisfactory, any variation within the sample is either insignificant or not a pressing concern, so accept the gage R&R study.

2. If the result of the calculations of repeatability is poor or marginal, you must address and define the existence of significant variation within the sample. The gage R&R study will have provided an estimate of σ_{EV} (equipment repeatability). If there is significant variation within the sample, this estimate is actually the estimate of

$$\sigma_{EV} = \sqrt{\sigma_R^2 + \sigma_V^2}$$

where σ_R estimates the actual sigma of repeatability and σ_V estimates the sigma of variation within the sample. We need to separate and estimate each component. It can not be done as the study was performed. We must perform a second study to estimate σ_V, allowing us to come back and obtain σ_{EV} from the equation above.

To estimate σ_R without the effect of σ_V, repeat the gage R&R study either with special samples that do not contain variation within them or by specifying exactly where on the production sample the repeated measurements are to be made. Examples would be using standard test blocks in testing a hardness tester or specifying the exact point on a bar to test for out-of-roundness. This time, $\sigma_V = \sigma_{EV}$ of the second study.

Use this value in the prior equation to solve for σ_V. For example, assume in the gage R&R study of a profilometer that $\sigma_{EV} = 2.33$, in this case an undesirable result. The design of the study permitted the variation within the sample to be mixed with that of repeatability:

$$\sigma_{EV} = 2.33 = \sqrt{\sigma_R^2 + \sigma_V^2}$$

Assume the study is reexecuted, only this time the point of measurement is controlled. The new estimate is $\sigma_R = 1.21 = \sigma_{EV}$ of the second study:

$$\sigma_{EV} = 2.33 = \sqrt{\sigma_R^2 + \sigma_V^2} = \sqrt{1.21^2 + \sigma_V^2}$$

$$\sigma_{EV} = 5.43 = 1.46 + \sigma_V^2$$

$$\sigma_V^2 = 3.97$$

$$\sigma_V = 1.99$$

Thus, we have found an estimate of σ_{EV} that does not include σ_V. We have also obtained an estimate of σ_V. In this example, we could continue to measure the gage R&R results based on the "clean" estimate of σ_{EV}. This will indicate our ability to measure. Note that the actual, routine measurements will be more variable than indicated by the R&R if σ_V (the variation within the sample) is a significant contributor to the variation. In this example,

$$\sigma_{EV} = 2.33 = \sqrt{\sigma_R^2 + \sigma_V^2}$$

is the estimate of the combined effect of device repeatability and within-sample variation and

σ_R 1.21 is the estimate of repeatability without the effect of variation within the sample

σ_V 1.99 is the estimate of the variation within the sample that excludes repeatability

If measurements are made at randomly selected locations on the samples, that measurement variation contains the effect of both within-sample variation *and* repeatability of the measurement devices.

Figure 3.1 illustrates this situation (in interpreting Figure 3.1, remember that the variances are added, not the individual sigmas).

If the measurements now are made at the same location on each sample, then the measurement variation does not contain the effect of variation within the sample. In that case $\sigma_{EV} = \sigma_R$, and σ_V is not measured at all. Note that in this example, the estimation of repeatability is seriously influenced when variation within the sample is present.

The results of the variation within the sample are extremely important, providing vital information on the process control characteristics to be addressed. What do we do about these results? The fact that a "clean" estimate of gage R&R is now available does not mean that the variation within the sample can be ignored. That information must be brought forward to stimulate process improvement. There are two ways to indicate the significance of the variation within the sample (either of the two measurement capability indices can be used):

1. Calculate percentage of variation within the sample:

$$\frac{\sigma_V}{\sigma_t} \times 100$$

where σ_t is the total variation

2. Calculate % R&R plus variation within the sample:

$$\frac{\sqrt{\sigma_R^2 + \sigma_V^2 + \sigma_{AV}^2}}{\sigma_t} \times 100$$

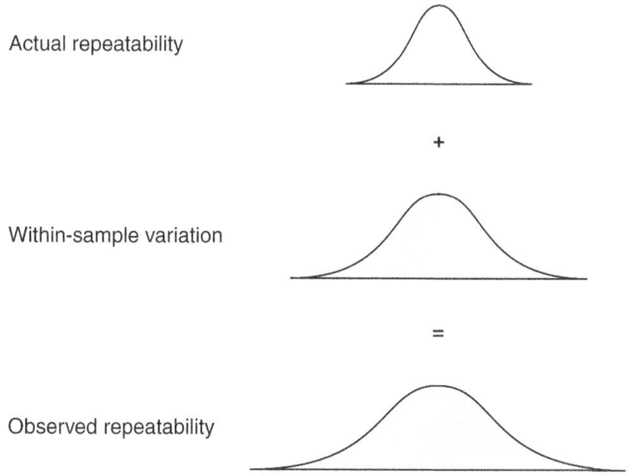

Actual repeatability

+

Within-sample variation

=

Observed repeatability

Figure 3.1   Actual repeatability, within-sample variation, and observed repeatability.

This allows the relative importance of the variations within the sample to be described and compared with *% EV* (equipment variation), *% AV* (appraiser variation), and *% R&R*.

CASE B: WE KNOW THERE IS SIGNIFICANT VARIATION WITHIN THE SAMPLE

The only difference between this situation and the previous case is the order of the successive R&R studies:

1. If you already know there is significant variation within the sample, then first perform the gage R&R study using whatever procedure will eliminate or avoid the variation within the sample. This may mean using standards or special samples, and/or carefully identifying and controlling the point of measurement. The resulting gage R&R study will estimate σ_{EV}, an estimate that is free of the within-sample variation, that is, $\sigma_{EV} = \sigma_R$. This study will provide the official gage R&R results.

2. Next, reexecute a gage R&R on production samples in a fashion that will produce the combined estimate of

$$\sigma_{EV} = \sqrt{\sigma_R^2 + \sigma_V^2}$$

Use the two sets of results to solve as before for σ_V. This second study will provide the estimate of variation within the sample.

Gage R&R studies are limited, by definition, to the effects of operators and the measurement device. Any indication or expectation of variation within the sample must be followed up with an appropriate study. Otherwise, our knowledge of the process is incomplete and may mislead the efforts to achieve improvement. To understand the measurement system, we must measure and understand this component of variation.

4

Performing a Traditional R&R Study

The standard manner of performing a gage R&R study utilizes the range method. This method is referred to in this book as the *traditional variables R&R study*. A minimum of two appraisers and 10 samples are used for the study. Each operator measures each sample at least twice, all using the same device. Each round of measurements on all the samples by an operator is called a *trial*. This approach allows the variability inherent in the device (repeatability) to be separated from the additional variability contributed by the variation between appraisers (reproducibility). Other sources of measurement variability (calibration, stability, linearity, and variation within the sample) in gage R&R are not addressed in this chapter. This approach commonly defines gage R&R in terms of an interval that contains 99.7% (6σ) of the theoretical distribution. Some organizations use different definitions. Some use a 99.0% (5.15σ) interval; others use a 95.0% (4σ) interval for defining intervals for repeatability, reproducibility, and overall gage R&R. To avoid confusion, clearly note which interval is used.

The original analysis techniques use ranges to estimate the results, and that is still the primary analytical approach taken here. This approach uses the parameters of statistical quality control to calculate estimates of various standard deviations. Gage R&R can also be analyzed as a designed experiment with components of variation estimated from an analysis of variance (ANOVA) (see Chapter 5). Regardless of the technique (range or ANOVA), the results are equivalent.

The criteria for assessment originally described the gage R&R results as a percentage of the process *specifications*. It has become more common to describe the results as a percentage of the process *variation*. The latter approach has the advantage of not being dependent on specifications that may be arbitrary. Each approach adds to the knowledge of the measurement situation.

The procedure presented here requires two or three appraisers. The recommended number of appraisers is three, which provides a better estimate of reproducibility. The procedures generate estimates of the standard deviations (σ) of repeatability, reproducibility, and overall gage R&R, providing measures of variability that can indicate improvement over time, regardless of changes in specifications or process performance. With one-sided specifications, only the standard deviations can be used. In addition, the 99.7% interval is estimated for repeatability, reproducibility, and gage R&R. The repeatability interval is referred to as *EV* for *equipment variation*; the reproducibility interval is referred to as *AV* for *appraiser variation*.

Table 4.1   Forbidden area.

# of trials	(# appraisers) × (# parts)												
	4	5	6	7	8	9	10	11	12	13	14	15	≥ 16
2	x	x	x	x	x	x	x	x	x	x	x	x	
3	x	x	x	x									
4	x												

The recommended number of trials for a given number of ranges (the number of appraisers × the number of parts) assures that the estimates of σEV are based on at least 14 degrees of freedom, the minimum for the case where number of appraisers × the number of parts is > 15 and there are two trials. If one does the study with 10 parts, two trials are sufficient if at least two appraisers are used. When the combinations of numbers of appraisers, parts, and trials fall into the "forbidden" area of the table, the level of confidence in the resulting estimates is reduced (see Table 4.1). Avoid these conditions where possible. This is also valid when there is a single operator (if there is no appraiser, assume a single appraiser). In that case, the rule concerning number of appraisers × the number of parts > 15 becomes simply the number of parts > 15. If the number of parts is 15 or less, then the number of trials should be increased accordingly.

The traditional method outputs can be assessed using process standard deviation, product tolerances, and/or the total variation from the study. These are the standard assessments discussed in Chapter 8. However, using total variation from the study is not recommended since this method assumes that the process variation can be represented accurately with the samples in the study. This is a very poor assumption for such a small sample size. The example provided will illustrate the typical output with the traditional approach using the product tolerance.

The parts used in the study should cover the range of measurements expected. However, there is also a requirement that the range of measurements used in the study be defined such that the average range on each part is expected to estimate a common σ_{EV}. If this homogeneity is not met, the results become erratic.

4.1 PERFORMING THE TRADITIONAL GAGE R&R STUDY

1. Determine the number of parts, trials, and appraisers necessary to conduct the study using a risk-based approach. To fully challenge the robustness and the ability of the measurement system, it is important to select some parts that are marginally considered good and marginally considered bad.

2. Establish the acceptability criteria based on health and safety risk.

3. Make sure the gage has adequate discrimination.

4. Verify the calibration status of the gage.

5. Ensure that each appraiser is properly trained and has the necessary competence to perform the study.

6. Allow sufficient time for environmental stabilization of the parts and gage if applicable.

7. Collect the data and complete the data sheet.

8. Calculate the ranges of the gage R&R study:

   - Compute the ranges of all repeated measurements by each appraiser.

   - Compute the average range for each appraiser ($\bar{R}$).

   - Compute the average of the average range for each appraiser ($\bar{\bar{R}}$).

   - Calculate the upper control limit (UCL) for the ranges, and check for lack of statistical control. Ranges exceeding the UCL should be repeated or dropped and the calculations redone. (Reasons for such "special causes" should be pursued.)

9. Calculate the performance statistics of the R&R study:

   - *Repeatability.* Also called *equipment variation* ($EV_{\text{Repeatability}}$). This is a 6σ range, estimating the spread that covers 99.7 percent of the measurement variation due solely to the gages.

   - *Reproducibility.* Also called *appraiser variation* ($AV_{\text{Reproducibility}}$). This is a 6σ range, estimating the spread that covers 99.7 percent of the measurement variation due solely to the operator.

   - *Repeatability and reproducibility.* Also called *gage R&R* (GRR). This is a 6σ range, estimating the spread that covers 99.7 percent of the variation due to the combination of these two sources.

10. Analyze the results and develop follow-up action as necessary.

11. Determine if guard banding is necessary (see Chapter 7).

12. Document the reevaluation criteria and interval.

A sample data sheet is shown in Figure 4.1. The formulas that follow are used to complete the study:

$$\bar{R}_{\text{Appraiser 1}} = \frac{R_1 + R_2 + R_3 + R_4 + R_5 + R_6 + R_7 + R_8 + R_9 + R_{10}}{c}$$

$$\bar{R}_{\text{Appraiser 2}} = \frac{R_1 + R_2 + R_3 + R_4 + R_5 + R_6 + R_7 + R_8 + R_9 + R_{10}}{c}$$

	Part #	1	2	3	4	5	6	7	8	9	10
Appraiser 1	1st trial										
	2nd trial										
	3rd trial										
	Range										
Appraiser 2	1st trial										
	2nd trial										
	3rd trial										
	Range										
Appraiser 3	1st trial										
	2nd trial										
	3rd trial										
	Range										

Figure 4.1   Traditional gage R&R template.

$$\bar{R}_{\text{Appraiser 3}} = \frac{R_1 + R_2 + R_3 + R_4 + R_5 + R_6 + R_7 + R_8 + R_9 + R_{10}}{c}$$

$$\bar{\bar{R}} = \frac{\bar{R}_{\text{Appraiser 1}} + \bar{R}_{\text{Appraiser 2}} + \bar{R}_{\text{Appraiser 3}}}{r}$$

$$\text{UCL} = D_4 \times \bar{\bar{R}}$$

$$\bar{X}_{\text{Appraiser 1}} = \frac{\Sigma\left(X_{\text{Appraiser 1}}\right)}{c \times t}$$

$$\bar{X}_{\text{Appraiser 2}} = \frac{\Sigma\left(X_{\text{Appraiser 2}}\right)}{c \times t}$$

$$\bar{X}_{\text{Appraiser 3}} = \frac{\Sigma\left(X_{\text{Appraiser 3}}\right)}{c \times t}$$

$$\bar{X}_{\text{Range}} = \max - \min\left(\bar{X}_{\text{Appraiser 1}}, \bar{X}_{\text{Appraiser 2}}, \bar{X}_{\text{Appraiser 3}}\right)$$

$$\sigma_{EV} = \frac{\bar{\bar{R}}}{C_2}$$

where C_2 is found in Appendix B, C_2 Correction Factors, with $Z = c \times r$, and $W = t$

$$\sigma_{AV} = \frac{X_{Range}}{C_2}$$

where C_2 is found in Appendix B, C_2 Correction Factors, with $Z = 1$, and $W = r$

$$\sigma_{RR} = \sqrt{\sigma_{EV}^2 + \sigma_{AV}^2}$$

$$EV(repeatability) = \frac{\sigma_{EV} \times 6}{TT \times 100}$$

$$AV(reproducibility) = \frac{\sqrt{(\sigma_{AV} \times 6)^2 - \frac{(\sigma_{EV} \times 6)^2}{c \times r}}}{TT \times 100}$$

(If the calculated value of the σ_{EV} variance is negative, set the value to zero.)

$$GRR = \sqrt{EV^2 + AV^2}$$

where

N = Total number of observations or $(r \times c \times t)$

r = Number of appraisers

c = Number of parts

t = Number of trials

TT = Total tolerance

D_4 = For t trials (See Appendix A, Control Chart Constants)

C_2 = See Appendix B, C_2 Correction Factors

4.2 GAGE R&R TRADITIONAL EXAMPLE

Example: A supplier is concerned about the ability to measure a specific feature in order to adequately assess the product against the customer specifications. Ten samples were tested three times by each of three operators (see Figure 4.2). (Note that this method easily handles any number of samples, operators, and trials as long as the rules in Table 4.1 are followed.) The acceptable specification for the feature is USL650 – LSL350 (total tolerance is 300). The process has a historical process standard deviation of 50:

Part #	1	2	3	4	5	6	7	8	9	10
1st trial	471	765	328	446	456	443	552	477	521	384
2nd trial	484	742	326	433	454	450	557	479	508	371
3rd trial	480	755	329	441	455	446	555	481	507	379
Range	13	23	3	13	2	7	5	4	14	13
1st trial	483	793	325	438	453	449	551	478	541	370
2nd trial	474	801	308	444	455	449	545	486	534	379
3rd trial	479	779	308	453	461	453	541	485	523	383
Range	9	22	17	15	8	4	10	8	18	13
1st trial	485	781	328	455	470	460	551	499	523	390
2nd trial	480	807	314	445	461	455	547	492	540	385
3rd trial	483	791	312	457	465	457	545	489	527	387
Range	5	26	16	12	9	5	6	10	17	5

(Appraiser 1 spans the first four rows; Appraiser 2 the next four; Appraiser 3 the last four.)

Figure 4.2   Completed traditional gage R&R template.

$$\bar{R}_{\text{Appraiser 1}} = \frac{R_1 + R_2 + R_3 + R_4 + R_5 + R_6 + R_7 + R_8 + R_9 + R_{10}}{c}$$

$$= \frac{13 + 23 + 3 + 13 + 2 + 7 + 5 + 4 + 14 + 13}{10}$$

$$= 9.7$$

$$\bar{R}_{\text{Appraiser 2}} = \frac{R_1 + R_2 + R_3 + R_4 + R_5 + R_6 + R_7 + R_8 + R_9 + R_{10}}{c}$$

$$= \frac{9 + 22 + 17 + 15 + 8 + 4 + 10 + 8 + 18 + 13}{10}$$

$$= 12.4$$

$$\bar{R}_{\text{Appraiser 3}} = \frac{R_1 + R_2 + R_3 + R_4 + R_5 + R_6 + R_7 + R_8 + R_9 + R_{10}}{c}$$

$$= \frac{5 + 26 + 16 + 12 + 9 + 5 + 6 + 10 + 17 + 5}{10}$$

$$= 11.1$$

$$\bar{\bar{R}} = \frac{\bar{R}_{\text{Appraiser 1}} + \bar{R}_{\text{Appraiser 2}} + \bar{R}_{\text{Appraiser 3}}}{r}$$

$$= \frac{9.7 + 12.4 + 11.1}{3}$$

$$= 11.1$$

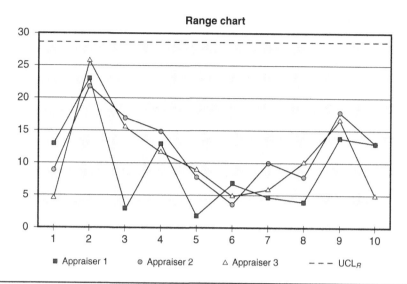

Figure 4.3 Range chart

$$\text{UCL}_R = D_4 \times \bar{R} = 2.574 \times 11.1 = 28.6$$

The ranges for each appraiser have been plotted along with the UCL_R in the range chart displayed in Figure 4.3. None of the points are beyond the UCL_R of 28.6, indicating that the measurements are in a state of statistical control. Therefore, we can continue with the example.

$$\bar{\bar{X}}_{\text{Appraiser 1}} = \frac{\Sigma\left(X_{\text{Appraiser 1}}\right)}{c \times t} = \frac{14475}{10 \times 3} = 482.5$$

$$\bar{\bar{X}}_{\text{Appraiser 2}} = \frac{\Sigma\left(X_{\text{Appraiser 2}}\right)}{c \times t} = \frac{14621}{10 \times 3} = 487.4$$

$$\bar{\bar{X}}_{\text{Appraiser 3}} = \frac{\Sigma\left(X_{\text{Appraiser 3}}\right)}{c \times t} = \frac{14781}{10 \times 3} = 492.7$$

$$X_{\text{Range}} = \max - \min\left(\bar{\bar{X}}_{\text{Appraiser 1}}, \bar{\bar{X}}_{\text{Appraiser 2}}, \bar{\bar{X}}_{\text{Appraiser 3}}\right) = 492.7 - 482.5 = 10.2$$

$$\sigma_{EV} = \frac{\bar{\bar{R}}}{C_2} = \frac{11.1}{1.693} = 6.56$$

$$\sigma_{AV} = \frac{X_{\text{Range}}}{C_2} = \frac{10.2}{1.912} = 5.33$$

$$\sigma_{RR} = \sqrt{\sigma_{EV}^2 + \sigma_{AV}^2} = \sqrt{6.56^2 + 5.33^2} = 8.45$$

Table 4.2   Gage acceptability criteria.

Gage R&R	Acceptance
< 10%	Acceptable
10%–30%	Marginally acceptable
> 30%	Unacceptable

$$EV(\text{repeatability}) = \frac{(\sigma_{EV} \times 6)}{TT \times 100} = \frac{6.56 \times 6}{300 \times 100} = 13.12\%$$

$$AV(\text{reproducibility}) = \frac{\sqrt{(\sigma_{AV} \times 6)^2 - \frac{(\sigma_{EV} \times 6)^2}{c \times r}}}{TT \times 100}$$

$$= \frac{\sqrt{(5.33 \times 6)^2 - \frac{(6.56 \times 6)^2}{10 \times 3}}}{300 \times 100} = 10.38\%$$

$$GRR = \sqrt{EV^2 + AV^2} = \sqrt{13.12^2 + 10.38^2} = 16.73\%$$

The gage R&R is 16.73% of the total tolerance of 300. According to Table 4.2, this gage is considered to be marginally acceptable. If the part being measured is deemed critical to health and/or safety, consider guard banding (see Chapter 7).

See Section 8.6 for the calculations for the measurement and process capability indices.

4.3 THE NUMBER OF DISTINCT CATEGORIES (N_{DC})

Number of distinct categories (N_{DC}) is the number of categories that the measurement system can distinguish and is directly related to the discrimination of the gage. This calculation is generally unnecessary due to the relationship between gage R&R and the N_{DC}. Figure 4.4 depicts the relationship between the number of distinct categories and the corresponding gage R&R values.

The use of 3 as a multiplier provides 99.7% confidence; ±3 standard deviations covers 99.7% of the normal population. The N_{DC} can generally be interpreted as acceptable for any number greater than 5:

$$N_{DC} = \sqrt{2 \times \left[\left(\frac{100}{GRR\%}\right)^2 - 1\right]}$$

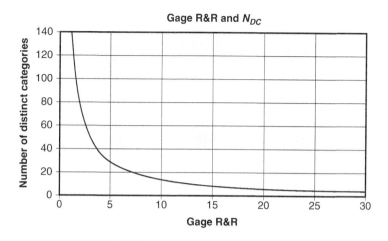

Figure 4.4   Relationship between the number of distinct categories and the corresponding gage R&R values.

Source: Based on information provided by Gary Phillips, used with permission.

where

$GRR\%$ = The overall gage R&R percentage

Example: A gage R&R study was conducted on a measuring system used to measure a machined part. The study resulted in a gage R&R of 16.23%. Calculate the N_{DC} for this study:

$$N_{DC} = \sqrt{2 \times \left[\left(\frac{100}{GRR\%} \right)^2 - 1 \right]} = \sqrt{2 \times \left[\left(\frac{100}{16.23} \right)^2 - 1 \right]} = 8.60$$

or 8 distinct categories.

5
Performing an ANOVA Gage R&R Study

Range estimates for small subgroups are nearly as powerful as the computations from *analysis of variance* (ANOVA) and much easier to explain or interpret. ANOVA offers a check on appraiser–part interaction that is not available with the range method, and requires more statistical knowledge to interpret and explain. Due to the simplicity of the approach, the range methods have been more widely used. The following is presented to support those who prefer to use the ANOVA method. There are two major differences between the range (traditional) method and the ANOVA approaches to gage R&R studies.

The effectiveness of the ANOVA method can be enhanced with the use of a range chart to evaluate the presence of special causes during the R&R study. The *R* chart serves to validate the stability of the measurement process and indicate problems that should be addressed immediately, before further analysis. Such occurrences are screened from subsequent calculations to better estimate the performance of a stable measurement process.

The ANOVA method computes the interaction between operators and samples and adds this source of variation to the reproducibility source. The range method assumes that there is no interaction between well-trained operators and the samples. In other words, all operators are assumed able to test each sample with equivalent precision. The use of well-trained operators generally is sufficient to avoid the presence of a significant interaction. The review of the control chart of ranges is also a weak check on the assumption of no interaction. Use of the interaction term provides a better estimate of reproducibility if there is an interaction. If the ANOVA procedure uses the estimate of the interaction component regardless of whether that term is statistically significant, the assessment of reproducibility will be slightly inflated.

If the interaction term is not reported separately due to being insignificant, it then becomes part of the error. In reality, these differences in methods generally have minor impact on the evaluation of a stable measurement process. The ANOVA method should be used in the case of destructive testing to help separate the variation components and possible interactions (confounding).

The recommended number of trials for a given number of ranges (the number of appraisers × the number of parts) assures that the estimates of σ_{EV} are based on at least 14 degrees of freedom, the minimum for the case where the number of appraisers × the number of parts > 15 and there are two trials. If one does the study with 10 samples, two trials are sufficient if at least two operators are used. When the combinations of numbers

Table 5.1   Forbidden area.

# of trials	(# appraisers) × (# parts)												
	4	5	6	7	8	9	10	11	12	13	14	15	≥ 16
2	X	X	X	X	X	X	X	X	X	X	X	X	
3	X	X	X	X									
4	X												

of appraisers, parts, and trials fall into the "forbidden" area of the table, the level of confidence in the resulting estimates is reduced (see Table 5.1). Avoid these conditions where possible. This is also valid when there is a single appraiser (if there is no appraiser, assume a single appraiser). In that case, the rule concerning the number of appraisers × number of parts > 15 becomes simply the number of parts > 15. If the number of parts is 15 or less, then the number of trials should be increased accordingly.

The parts used in the study should cover the range of measurements expected. However, there is also a requirement that the range of measurements used in the study be defined such that the average range on each part is expected to estimate a common σ_{EV}. If this homogeneity is not met, the results become erratic.

The ANOVA calculations demonstrated in this book utilize the appraiser–part interaction. If appraiser–part interaction is not used, the ANOVA results will be very similar to those from the use of the range methods. If the appraiser–part interaction is used, the results for reproducibility and total gage R&R will be larger than the estimates of the range methods by the addition of this interaction component of variance. Note that presence of a significant interaction requires investigation or *root cause analysis* (RCA) to determine why it occurred.

The two-way ANOVA is used when there are more than one independent variable and multiple observations for each independent variable, as is the case in gage R&R studies. The two-way ANOVA can not only determine the main effect of the contributions of each independent variable but also identifies whether there is a significant interaction effect between the independent variables.

When conducting the gage R&R, if F calculated is greater than F critical for appraisers, parts, and appraisers × parts, they are considered to be statistically significant and must be used in the further calculations to determine the gage R&R. If, however, F calculated is less than or equal to F critical for any of the terms, they are considered statistically insignificant and combined with the within (error) term—also known as *repeatability* (see Appendix C, Selected Percentages of the F-Distribution).

The ANOVA outputs can be assessed using the process standard deviation, product tolerance, and/or the total variation from the study. However, using total variation from the study is not recommended since this method assumes that the process variation can be represented accurately with the samples in the study. This is a very poor assumption for such a small sample size. The example provided illustrates the typical output with the ANOVA approach using product tolerance.

5.1 PERFORMING THE ANOVA GAGE R&R STUDY

1. Determine the number of parts, trials, and appraisers necessary to conduct the study using a risk-based approach.

2. Establish the acceptability criteria based on risk.

3. Allow sufficient time for environmental stabilization of the parts and gage if applicable.

4. Make sure the gage has adequate discrimination.

5. Ensure that the gage used for the study has been calibrated.

6. Ensure that each appraiser is properly trained and has the necessary competence to perform the study.

7. To fully challenge the robustness and the ability of the measurement system, it is important to select some parts that are marginally considered good and marginally considered bad.

8. Collect the data and complete the two-way ANOVA data sheet.

9. Calculate the ranges of the gage R&R study:

   • Compute the ranges of all repeated measurements by each appraiser.

   • Compute the average range for each appraiser ($\bar{R}$).

   • Compute the average of the average range for each appraiser ($\bar{\bar{R}}$).

   • Calculate the upper control limit (UCL_R) for the ranges.

   • Plot the range for each part for each appraiser and check for lack of statistical control. Ranges exceeding the UCL should be repeated or dropped and the calculations redone. (Reasons for such "special causes" should be pursued.)

10. Complete the ANOVA summary table.

11. Determine whether the interaction is statistically significant.

12. Calculate the variances.

13. Calculate the performance statistics of the R&R study:

   • *Repeatability.* Also called *equipment variation* ($EV_{Repeatability}$). This is a 6σ range, estimating the spread that covers 99.7% of the measurement variation due solely to the gages.

   • *Reproducibility.* Also called *appraiser variation* ($AV_{Reproducibility}$). This is a 6σ range, estimating the spread that covers 99.7% of the measurement variation due solely to the operator.

- *Repeatability and reproducibility.* Also called *gage R&R* (GRR). This is a 6σ range, estimating the spread that covers 99.7% of the variation due to the combination of these two sources.

14. Analyze the results and develop follow-up action as necessary.

15. Determine whether guard banding is necessary.

16. Document the reevaluation criteria and interval.

A sample data sheet is shown in Figure 5.1, a two-way ANOVA summary table is depicted in Table 5.2, and Table 5.3 shows a two-way ANOVA variance table. The formulas that follow are used to complete the study.

	Part #	1	2	3	4	5	6	7	8	9	10
Appraiser 1	1st trial										
	2nd trial										
	3rd trial										
	Range										
Appraiser 2	1st trial										
	2nd trial										
	3rd trial										
	Range										
Appraiser 3	1st trial										
	2nd trial										
	3rd trial										
	Range										

Figure 5.1   Two-way ANOVA data sheet.

Table 5.2   Two-way ANOVA summary table.

Source of variation	SS	df	MS	*F* calc	*F* crit
Appraisers					
Parts					
Appraisers × Parts (interaction)					
Within (error)					
Total					

where
    SS = Sum of squares
    df = Degrees of freedom
    MS = Mean square

Table 5.3   Two-way ANOVA variance
table.

Source of variation	Variance (σ^2)
Appraisers	
Parts	
Appraisers × Parts	
Repeatability	

$$\bar{R}_{\text{Appraiser 1}} = \frac{R_1 + R_2 + R_3 + R_4 + R_5 + R_6 + R_7 + R_8 + R_9 + R_{10}}{c}$$

$$\bar{R}_{\text{Appraiser 2}} = \frac{R_1 + R_2 + R_3 + R_4 + R_5 + R_6 + R_7 + R_8 + R_9 + R_{10}}{c}$$

$$\bar{R}_{\text{Appraiser 3}} = \frac{R_1 + R_2 + R_3 + R_4 + R_5 + R_6 + R_7 + R_8 + R_9 + R_{10}}{c}$$

$$\bar{\bar{R}} = \frac{\bar{R}_{\text{Appraiser 1}} + \bar{R}_{\text{Appraiser 2}} + \bar{R}_{\text{Appraiser 3}}}{r}$$

$$\text{UCL}_R = D_4 \times \bar{\bar{R}}$$

$$\text{SS}_{\text{Total}} = \Sigma X_N^2 - \frac{(\Sigma X_N)^2}{N}$$

$$\text{SS}_{\text{Between}} = \frac{(\Sigma X_1)^2}{n_1} + \frac{(\Sigma X_2)^2}{n_2} + \ldots + \frac{(\Sigma X_k)^2}{n_k} - \frac{(\Sigma X_N)^2}{N}$$

Please note that this formula requires data from each individual cell. For example, Part 1—Appraiser 1, Part 2—Appraiser 1 . . . Part 9—Appraiser 3, Part 10—Appraiser 3.

$$\text{SS}_{\text{Within}} = \text{SS}_{\text{Total}} - \text{SS}_{\text{Between}}$$

$$\text{SS}_{\text{Appraisers}} = \Sigma \frac{(\Sigma \text{ for each Appraisers})^2}{n \text{ for each Appraisers}} - \frac{(\Sigma X_N)^2}{N}$$

$$\text{SS}_{\text{Parts}} = \Sigma \frac{(\Sigma \text{ for each Part})^2}{n \text{ for each Part}} - \frac{(\Sigma X_N)^2}{N}$$

$$\text{SS}_{\text{Interaction}} = \text{SS}_{\text{Between}} - \text{SS}_{\text{Appraisers}} - \text{SS}_{\text{Parts}}$$

$$\text{df}_{\text{Total}} = N - 1$$

$$df_{Appraisers} = r - 1$$

$$df_{Parts} = c - 1$$

$$df_{Appraisers \times Parts} = (r - 1)(c - 1)$$

$$df_{Within} = N - rc$$

$$MS_{Within} = \frac{SS_{Within}}{df_{Within}}$$

$$MS_{Appraisers} = \frac{SS_{Appraisers}}{df_{Appraisers}}$$

$$MS_{Parts} = \frac{SS_{Parts}}{df_{Parts}}$$

$$MS_{Appraisers \times Parts} = \frac{SS_{Appraisers \times Parts}}{df_{Appraisers \times Parts}}$$

$$F_{Appraisers} = \frac{MS_{Appraisers}}{MS_{Within}}$$

$$F_{Parts} = \frac{MS_{Parts}}{MS_{Within}}$$

$$F_{Appraisers \times Parts} = \frac{MS_{Appraisers \times Parts}}{MS_{Within}}$$

$$\sigma^2_{Repeatability} = MS_{Within}$$

$$\sigma^2_{Appraisers \times Parts} = \frac{MS_{Appraisers \times Parts} - MS_{Within}}{t}$$

(If the calculated value of the variance is negative, set the value to zero)

$$\sigma^2_{Parts} = \frac{MS_{Parts} - MS_{Appraisers \times Parts}}{r \times t}$$

$$\sigma^2_{Appraisers} = \frac{MS_{Appraisers} - MS_{Appraisers \times Parts}}{r \times c}$$

$$\sigma_{EV} = \sqrt{MS_{Within}}$$

$$\sigma_{AV} = \sqrt{\sigma^2_{Appraisers} + \sigma^2_{Appraisers \times Parts}}$$

$$\sigma_{RR} = \sqrt{\sigma_{EV}^2 + \sigma_{AV}^2}$$

$$EV(\text{repeatability}) = \frac{\sqrt{\sigma_{\text{Repeatability}}^2} \times 6}{TT \times 100}$$

$$AV(\text{reproducibility}) = \frac{\sqrt{\sigma_{\text{Appraisers}}^2 + \sigma_{\text{Appraisers} \times \text{Parts}}^2} \times 6}{TT \times 100}$$

$$GRR = \sqrt{EV^2 + AV^2} \times 100$$

where

N = Total number of observations, or (r × c × t)

r = Number of appraisers

c = Number of parts

t = Number of trials

TT = Total tolerance

D_4 = For t trials (See Appendix A, Control Chart Constants)

F_{Critical} = α, df, df values of the F-distribution (See Appendix C, Selected Percentages of the F-Distribution)

5.2 GAGE R&R ANOVA EXAMPLE WITH INTERACTION

Example: A supplier is concerned about the ability to measure a specific feature in order to adequately assess the product against the customer specifications. Ten samples were tested three times by each of three operators (see Figure 5.2). (Note that the ANOVA method easily handles any number of samples, operators, and trials as long as the rules in Table 5.1 are followed.) The acceptable specification for the feature is USL650 – LSL350 (total tolerance is 300). The process has a historical process standard deviation of 50.

$$\begin{aligned}
\bar{R}_{\text{Appraiser 1}} &= \frac{R_1 + R_2 + R_3 + R_4 + R_5 + R_6 + R_7 + R_8 + R_9 + R_{10}}{c} \\
&= \frac{13 + 23 + 3 + 13 + 2 + 7 + 5 + 4 + 14 + 13}{10} \\
&= 9.7
\end{aligned}$$

	Part #	1	2	3	4	5	6	7	8	9	10
Appraiser 1	**1st trial**	471	765	328	446	456	443	552	477	521	384
	2nd trial	484	742	326	433	454	450	557	479	508	371
	3rd trial	480	755	329	441	455	446	555	481	507	379
	Range	13	23	3	13	2	7	5	4	14	13
Appraiser 2	**1st trial**	483	793	325	438	453	449	551	478	541	370
	2nd trial	474	801	308	444	455	449	545	486	534	379
	3rd trial	479	779	308	453	461	453	541	485	523	383
	Range	9	22	17	15	8	4	10	8	18	13
Appraiser 3	**1st trial**	485	781	328	455	470	460	551	499	523	390
	2nd trial	480	807	314	445	461	455	547	492	540	385
	3rd trial	483	791	312	457	465	457	545	489	527	387
	Range	5	26	16	12	9	5	6	10	17	5

Figure 5.2   Completed two-way ANOVA data sheet.

$$\bar{R}_{\text{Appraiser 2}} = \frac{R_1 + R_2 + R_3 + R_4 + R_5 + R_6 + R_7 + R_8 + R_9 + R_{10}}{c}$$

$$= \frac{9 + 22 + 17 + 15 + 8 + 4 + 10 + 8 + 18 + 13}{10}$$

$$= 12.4$$

$$\bar{R}_{\text{Appraiser 3}} = \frac{R_1 + R_2 + R_3 + R_4 + R_5 + R_6 + R_7 + R_8 + R_9 + R_{10}}{c}$$

$$= \frac{5 + 26 + 16 + 12 + 9 + 5 + 6 + 10 + 17 + 5}{10}$$

$$= 11.1$$

$$\bar{\bar{R}} = \frac{\bar{R}_{\text{Appraiser 1}} + \bar{R}_{\text{Appraiser 2}} + \bar{R}_{\text{Appraiser 3}}}{r}$$

$$= \frac{9.7 + 12.4 + 11.1}{3}$$

$$= 11.1$$

$$\text{UCL}_R = D_4 \times \bar{\bar{R}} = 2.574 \times 11.1 = 28.6$$

The ranges for each appraiser have been plotted along with the UCL_R in the range chart displayed in Figure 5.3. None of the points are beyond the UCL_R of 28.6, indicating that the measurements are in a state of statistical control. Therefore, we can continue with the example by completing the ANOVA table.

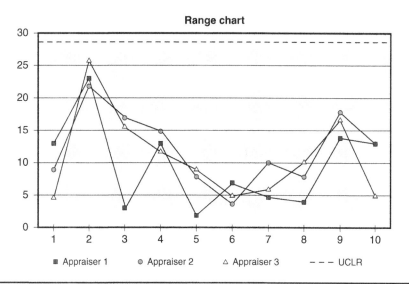

Figure 5.3   Range chart.

$$SS_{Total} = \Sigma X_N^2 - \frac{(\Sigma X_N)^2}{N} = 22603175 - \frac{(43877)^2}{90} = 1212162.5$$

$$SS_{Between} = \frac{(\Sigma X_1)^2}{n_1} + \frac{(\Sigma X_2)^2}{n_2} + \ldots + \frac{(\Sigma X_k)^2}{n_k} - \frac{(\Sigma X_N)^2}{N}$$

$$= \frac{(1435)^2}{3} + \frac{(2262)^2}{3} + \ldots + \frac{(1590)^2}{3} + \frac{(1162)^2}{3} - \frac{(43877)^2}{90} = 1209592.5$$

$$SS_{Within} = SS_{Total} - SS_{Between} = 1212162.5 - 1209592.5 = 2570.0$$

$$SS_{Appraisers} = \Sigma \frac{(\Sigma \text{ for each Appraiser})^2}{n \text{ for each Appraiser}} - \frac{(\Sigma X_N)^2}{N}$$

$$= \frac{(14475)^2}{30} + \frac{(14621)^2}{30} + \frac{(14781)^2}{30} - \frac{(43877)^2}{90}$$

$$= 1561.5$$

$$SS_{Parts} = \Sigma \frac{(\Sigma \text{ for each Part})^2}{n \text{ for each Part}} - \frac{(\Sigma X_N)^2}{N}$$

$$= \frac{(4139)^2}{9} + \frac{(7014)^2}{9} + \ldots + \frac{(4724)^2}{9} + \frac{(3428)^2}{9} - \frac{(43877)^2}{90}$$

$$= 1204340.5$$

$$SS_{\text{Interaction}} = SS_{\text{Between}} - SS_{\text{Appraisers}} - SS_{\text{Parts}}$$

$$= 1209595.2 - 1561.5 - 1204340.5 = 3690.5$$

$$df_{\text{Total}} = N - 1 = 90 - 1 = 89$$

$$df_{\text{Appraisers}} = r - 1 = 3 - 1 = 2$$

$$df_{\text{Parts}} = c - 1 = 10 - 1 = 9$$

$$df_{\text{Appraisers} \times \text{Parts}} = (r - 1)(c - 1) = (3 - 1)(10 - 1) = 18$$

$$df_{\text{Within}} = N - rc = 90 - (3 \times 10) = 60$$

$$MS_{\text{Within}} = \frac{SS_{\text{Within}}}{df_{\text{Within}}} = \frac{2570.0}{60} = 42.8$$

$$MS_{\text{Appraisers}} = \frac{SS_{\text{Appraisers}}}{df_{\text{Appraisers}}} = \frac{1561.5}{2} = 780.8$$

$$MS_{\text{Parts}} = \frac{SS_{\text{Parts}}}{df_{\text{Parts}}} = \frac{1204340.5}{9} = 133815.6$$

$$MS_{\text{Appraisers} \times \text{Parts}} = \frac{SS_{\text{Appraisers} \times \text{Parts}}}{df_{\text{Appraisers} \times \text{Parts}}} = \frac{3690.5}{18} = 205.0$$

$$F_{\text{Appraisers}} = \frac{MS_{\text{Appraisers}}}{MS_{\text{Within}}} = \frac{780.8}{42.8} = 18.24$$

$$F_{\text{Parts}} = \frac{MS_{\text{Parts}}}{MS_{\text{Within}}} = \frac{133815.6}{42.8} = 3126.53$$

$$F_{\text{Appraisers} \times \text{Parts}} = \frac{MS_{\text{Appraisers} \times \text{Parts}}}{MS_{\text{Within}}} = \frac{205.0}{42.8} = 4.79$$

Results for Appraisers

Since *F* calculated is greater than *F* critical, it is considered to be statistically significant and must be used in the further calculations to determine the overall gage R&R (see Figure 5.4 and Tables 5.4 and 5.5).

Results for Parts

Since *F* calculated is greater than *F* critical, it is considered to be statistically significant and must be used in the further calculations to determine the overall gage R&R (see Figure 5.5 and Tables 5.4 and 5.5).

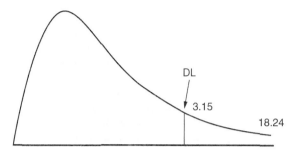

Figure 5.4   Decision limit appraisers.

Table 5.4   Completed two-way ANOVA summary table.

Source of variation	SS	df	MS	F calc	F crit
Appraisers	1561.5	2	780.8	18.24	3.15
Parts	1204340.5	9	133815.6	3126.53	2.04
Appraisers × Parts (interaction)	3690.5	18	205.0	4.79	1.78
Within (error)	2570.0	60	42.8		
Total	1212162.5	89			

Table 5.5   Completed two-way ANOVA variance table.

Source of variation	Variance (σ^2)
Appraisers	19.2
Parts	14845.6
Appraisers × Parts	54.1
Repeatability	42.8

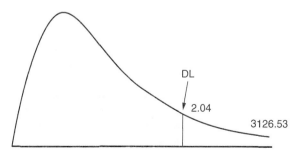

Figure 5.5   Decision limit parts.

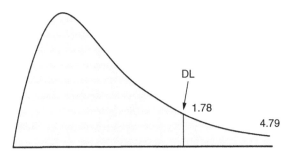

Figure 5.6 Decision limit interaction (appraisers and parts).

Results for Interactions (Appraisers and Parts)

Since F calculated is greater than F critical, it is considered to be statistically significant and must be used in the further calculations to determine the overall gage R&R (see Figure 5.6 and Tables 5.4 and 5.5).

Note: We will finish this example with all of the terms and then demonstrate the process of removing terms and combining them with the within (error) term—also known as *repeatability*.

$$\sigma^2_{\text{Repeatability}} = MS_{\text{Within}} = 42.8$$

$$\sigma^2_{\text{Appraisers} \times \text{Parts}} = \frac{MS_{\text{Appraisers} \times \text{Parts}} - MS_{\text{Within}}}{t} = \frac{205.0 - 42.8}{3} = 54.1$$

$$\sigma^2_{\text{Parts}} = \frac{MS_{\text{Parts}} - MS_{\text{Appraisers} \times \text{Parts}}}{r \times t} = \frac{133815.6 - 205.2}{3 \times 3} = 14845.6$$

$$\sigma^2_{\text{Appraisers}} = \frac{MS_{\text{Appraisers}} - MS_{\text{Appraisers} \times \text{Parts}}}{r \times c} = \frac{780.8 - 205.0}{3 \times 10} = 19.2$$

$$\sigma_{EV} = \sqrt{MS_{\text{Within}}} = \sqrt{42.8} = 6.54$$

$$\sigma_{AV} = \sqrt{\sigma^2_{\text{Appraisers}} + \sigma^2_{\text{Appraisers} \times \text{Parts}}} = \sqrt{19.2 + 54.1} = 8.56$$

$$\sigma_{RR} = \sqrt{\sigma^2_{EV} + \sigma^2_{AV}} = \sqrt{8.56^2 + 6.54^2} = 10.77$$

$$EV(\text{repeatability}) = \frac{\sqrt{\sigma^2_{\text{Repeatability}}} \times 6}{TT \times 100}$$

$$= \frac{\sqrt{42.8} \times 6}{300 \times 100} = 13.08\%$$

Table 5.6	Gage acceptability criteria.
Gage R&R	**Acceptance**
< 10%	Acceptable
10%–30%	Marginally acceptable
> 30%	Unacceptable

$$AV(\text{reproducibility}) = \frac{\sqrt{\sigma^2_{\text{Appraisers}} + \sigma^2_{\text{Appraisers} \times \text{Parts}}} \times 6}{TT \times 100}$$

$$= \frac{\sqrt{19.2 + 54.1} \times 6}{300 \times 100} = 17.12\%$$

$$GRR = \sqrt{EV^2 + AV^2} \times 100 = \sqrt{13.08^2 + 17.12^2} = 21.54\%$$

The gage R&R is 21.54% of the total tolerance of 300. According to Table 5.6, this gage is considered to be marginally acceptable. If the part being measured is deemed critical to health and/or safety, consider guard banding (see Chapter 7).

See Section 8.7 for the calculations for the measurement and process capability indices.

5.3 GAGE R&R ANOVA EXAMPLE WITHOUT INTERACTION

If a term is not statistically significant (F calculated is less than F critical), the term can be added to the within (error) term. For this example, we will use the completed two-way ANOVA summary Table 5.4. We will consider the Appraisers × Parts (interaction) term to be not statistically significant. Therefore, the Appraisers × Parts (interaction) SS and df were added to the within (error), causing us to recalculate the MS SS within (error)/within (error) df.

Results for Appraisers

Since F calculated is greater than F critical, it is considered to be statistically significant and must be used in the further calculations to determine the overall gage R&R (see Figure 5.7 and Tables 5.7 and 5.8).

Results for Parts

Since F calculated is greater than F critical, it is considered to be statistically significant and must be used in the further calculations to determine the overall gage R&R (see Figure 5.8 and Tables 5.7 and 5.8).

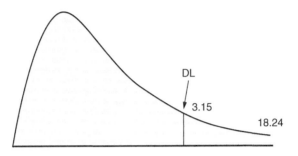

Figure 5.7   Decision limit appraisers.

Table 5.7   Completed two-way ANOVA summary table without interaction.

Source of variation	SS	df	MS	*F* calc	*F* crit
Appraisers	1561.5	2	780.8	18.24	3.15
Parts	1204340.5	9	133815.6	3126.53	2.04
Appraisers × Parts					
Within (error)	6260.5	78	80.3		
Total	1212162.5	89			

Table 5.8   Completed two-way ANOVA variance table without interaction.

Source of variation	Variance (σ^2)
Appraisers	23.4
Parts	14859.5
Appraisers × Parts	0.0
Repeatability	80.3

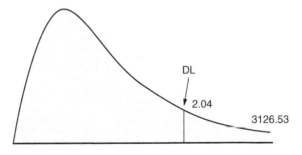

Figure 5.8   Decision limit parts.

$$\sigma^2_{\text{Repeatability}} = MS_{\text{Within}} = 80.3$$

$$\sigma^2_{\text{Parts}} = \frac{MS_{\text{Parts}} - MS_{\text{Within}}}{r \times t} = \frac{133815.6 - 80.3}{3 \times 3} = 14859.5$$

$$\sigma^2_{\text{Appraisers}} = \frac{MS_{\text{Appraisers}} - MS_{\text{Within}}}{r \times c} = \frac{780.8 - 80.3}{3 \times 10} = 23.4$$

$$EV(\text{repeatability}) = \frac{\sqrt{\sigma^2_{\text{Repeatability}}} \times 6}{TT \times 100}$$

$$= \frac{\sqrt{80.3} \times 6}{300 \times 100} = 17.92\%$$

$$AV(\text{reproducibility}) = \frac{\sqrt{\sigma^2_{\text{Appraisers}} + \sigma^2_{\text{Appraisers} \times \text{Parts}}} \times 6}{TT \times 100}$$

$$= \frac{\sqrt{23.4 + 0.0} \times 6}{300 \times 100} = 9.67\%$$

$$GRR = \sqrt{EV^2 + AV^2} \times 100 = \sqrt{17.92^2 + 9.67^2} = 20.36\%$$

The gage R&R is 20.36% of the total tolerance of 300. According to Table 5.6, this gage is considered to be marginally acceptable. If the part being measured is deemed critical to health and/or safety, consider guard banding (see Chapter 7, Measurement Uncertainty and Guard Banding).

5.4 GAGE R&R ANOVA EXAMPLE WITHOUT APPRAISER

We will now consider the appraisers term to be not statistically significant. Therefore, the appraisers SS and df were added to the within (error), causing us to recalculate the MS SS within (error)/within (error) df.

Results for Parts

Since *F* calculated is greater than *F* critical, it is considered to be statistically significant and must be used in the further calculations to determine the overall gage R&R (see Figure 5.9 and Table 5.9).

Using the information contained in Table 5.10, the gage R&R is 19.78% of the total tolerance of 300. According to Table 5.6, this gage is considered to be marginally acceptable. If the part being measured is deemed critical to health and/or safety, consider guard banding (see Chapter 7, Measurement Uncertainty and Guard Banding).

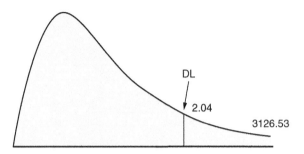

Figure 5.9   Decision limit parts.

Table 5.9   Completed two-way ANOVA summary table without appraiser.

Source of variation	SS	df	MS	F calc	F crit
Appraisers					
Parts	1204340.5	9	133815.6	3126.53	2.04
Appraisers × Parts					
Within (error)	7822.0	80	97.8		
Total	1212162.5	89			

Table 5.10   Completed two-way ANOVA variance table without appraiser.

Source of variation	Variance (σ^2)
Appraisers	0.0
Parts	14857.5
Appraisers × Parts	0.0
Repeatability	97.8

$$\sigma^2_{\text{Repeatability}} = \text{MS}_{\text{Within}} = 97.8$$

$$\sigma^2_{\text{Parts}} = \frac{\text{MS}_{\text{Parts}} - \text{MS}_{\text{Within}}}{r \times t} = \frac{133815.6 - 97.8}{3 \times 3} = 148575.5$$

$$EV(\text{repeatability}) = \frac{\sqrt{\sigma^2_{\text{Repeatability}}} \times 6}{TT \times 100}$$

$$= \frac{\sqrt{97.8} \times 6}{300 \times 100} = 19.78\%$$

$$AV(\text{reproducibility}) = \frac{\sqrt{\sigma^2_{\text{Appraisers}} + \sigma^2_{\text{Appraisers} \times \text{Parts}}} \times 6}{TT \times 100}$$

$$= \frac{\sqrt{0.0 + 0.0} \times 6}{300 \times 100} = 0.00\%$$

$$GRR = \sqrt{EV^2 + AV^2} \times 100 = \sqrt{19.78^2 + 0^2} = 19.78\%$$

6

Bias, Linearity, and Stability

Bias, linearity, and stability can have a significant influence on the measurement system. *Bias* is the difference of the measurement from the true but unknown value. *Linearity* considers the accuracy of the measurement system over the full range of the system. *Stability* assesses whether the measurement system changes over time. Since most measurements are within a narrowly defined tolerance band (USL–LSL), bias and linearity calculations are generally unnecessary. Stability is probably the most important and is generally addressed via the calibration program, but other factors such as environmental conditions may cause stability issues.

Accuracy is closely associated with the location of the distribution of measurements, and can be described by bias, linearity, and stability, whereas precision is closely related to the spread of the distribution of measurements and is described by repeatability and reproducibility. Figure 6.1 depicts the relationship between accuracy and precision, which can also be applied to the measurement system concepts of bias, linearity, stability, repeatability, and reproducibility.

Figure 6.2 shows the application of accuracy and precision.

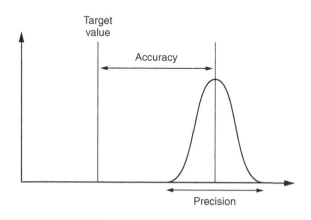

Figure 6.1   Relationship between the target value, accuracy, and precision.

Source: M. A. Durivage, *Practical Engineering, Process, and Reliability Engineering Statistics* (Milwaukee: ASQ Quality Press, 2014). Used with permission.

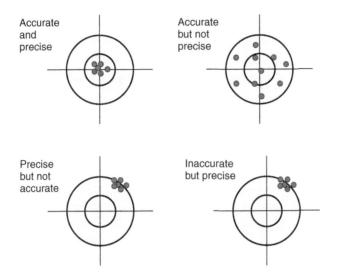

Figure 6.2   Accuracy versus precision.

Source: M. A. Durivage, *Practical Engineering, Process, and Reliability Engineering Statistics* (Milwaukee: ASQ Quality Press, 2014). Used with permission.

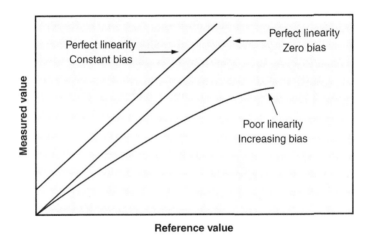

Figure 6.3   Bias and linearity.

    The relationship between bias and linearity is shown in Figure 6.3. A measurement system with perfect linearity and zero bias will display as a 45-degree angle when the measured value is plotted against a reference value. As shown by the line depicting perfect linearity and constant bias, there is a constant distinct shift of the measured values from the true or reference value. The last plotted line shows the case of poor linearity with an increasing bias. Although the measured value becomes larger as the true, or *reference*, value becomes larger, the function is not linear.

6.1 BIAS AND LINEARITY GRAPHICAL METHOD

Linearity can be described graphically and mathematically by a line that shows the relationship between the reference values and the measured values. Recall that linearity considers the accuracy of the measurement system over the full range of the system. To perform a linearity study, it is important to select five to seven parts that cover the range of expected outputs of the process. These parts will be considered the *reference parts*, and should be measured by one highly skilled technician or engineer so as not to introduce reproducibility into the calculations. The results are then plotted and analyzed visually to detect the presence of linearity. The plot uses the reference parts measurements (ordered from smallest to largest) on the *X* axis and the average measured values on the *Y* axis. It is recommended to measure each part 10 times and use the average value for this axis.

Example: The quality manager wishes to evaluate the linearity of a gage. The manager wishes to use seven parts that cover the range of the expected process outputs to assess the linearity. Seven parts are selected and measured by a highly skilled measurement engineer to establish the reference values, after which a quality technician measures the reference parts 10 times. The reference value average measured readings are recorded in Table 6.1. The acceptable specification for the feature is USL650 – LSL350 (total tolerance is 300). The process has a historical process standard deviation of 50.

The engineer then plots the results in a linearity plot as shown in Figure 6.4. Graphically, the results show a relatively straight line on a 45-degree angle, which indicates that the measuring device is linear.

6.2 BIAS AND LINEARITY ANALYTICAL METHOD

To mathematically evaluate bias and linearity, we must calculate the line of best fit using the reference values and the measured values with the equation

$$Y = aX + b$$

Table 6.1   Reference parts versus measured parts.

Reference parts	Measured parts
249	219
360	318
442	407
495	465
597	566
647	614
702	677

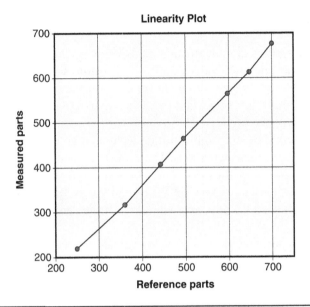

Figure 6.4   Linearity plot for the example.

where

Y = The measured value

a = Slope of the line

b = The Y intercept

X = The reference value

To calculate the slope:

$$a = \frac{n \times \Sigma XY - (\Sigma X)(\Sigma Y)}{n \times \Sigma X^2 - (\Sigma X)^2}$$

where

n = The number of reference parts

Y = The measured value

X = The reference value

To calculate the Y intercept:

$$b = \frac{\Sigma Y - (a \times \Sigma X)}{n}$$

where

X = The reference value

Y = The measured value

a = Slope of the line

n = The number of reference parts

Although using the data in Table 6.2 and displayed in Figure 6.4 the plot appeared to show a relatively straight line on a 45-degree angle, which indicates that the measuring device is linear, the quality manager wishes to evaluate the results mathematically. The manager also requires 95% confidence.

$$a = \frac{n + \Sigma XY - (\Sigma X)(\Sigma Y)}{n \times \Sigma X^2 - (\Sigma X)^2} = \frac{7 \times 1789494 - (3492)(3266)}{7 \times 1899812 - 3492^2} = 1.015$$

$$b = \frac{\Sigma Y - (a \times \Sigma X)}{n} = \frac{3266 - (1.015 \times 3492)}{7} = -39.769$$

The equation of the best fit line is

$$Y = aX + b$$

$$Y = 1.015X + (-39.769) \text{ or } Y = 1.015X - 39.769$$

6.3 CORRELATION ANALYSIS

Correlation analysis is the measure of strength or the degree of linear association between two variables. The correlation coefficient can vary from positive 1 (indicating a perfect positive relationship), through zero (indicating the absence of a relationship), to negative 1 (indicating a perfect negative relationship) (see Figure 6.5). As a rule of thumb, correlation coefficients between .00 and .30 are considered weak, those between .30 and .70 are moderate, and coefficients between .70 and 1.00 are considered high. However, this rule should always be qualified by a visual inspection of the plotted points.

To further test the significance of the calculated correlation coefficient, the calculated value can be compared to a correlation coefficient critical value (see Appendix D, Critical Values of the Correlation Coefficient). If the absolute value of r is greater than the critical table value, then it can be stated that you are confident $(1 - \alpha)$ that there is a statistically significant relationship between the X (reference value) and Y (measured values).

To calculate the correlation coefficient:

$$r = \frac{n \times \Sigma XY - \Sigma X \times \Sigma Y}{\sqrt{n \times \Sigma X^2 - (\Sigma X)^2} \times \sqrt{n \times \Sigma Y^2 - (\Sigma Y)^2}}$$

Table 6.2   Summary data table for the example.

X	Y	X²	Y²	a	b	Y²–b	Y–a	(X–Xavg)²	XY
249	219	62001	47961	1.015	–39.769	48000.8	218.0	62400.0	54531
360	318	129600	101124	1.015	–39.769	101163.8	317.0	19265.5	114480
442	407	195364	165649	1.015	–39.769	165688.8	406.0	3226.2	179894
495	465	245025	216225	1.015	–39.769	216264.8	464.0	14.4	230175
597	566	356049	320356	1.015	–39.769	320395.8	565.0	9643.2	337902
647	614	418609	376996	1.015	–39.769	377035.8	613.0	21963.2	397258
702	677	492804	458329	1.015	–39.769	458368.8	676.0	41290.2	475254
Sum	3492	3266	1899812	1686640			1686918.4	3258.9	157802.9	1789494
Avg	498.8	466.6								

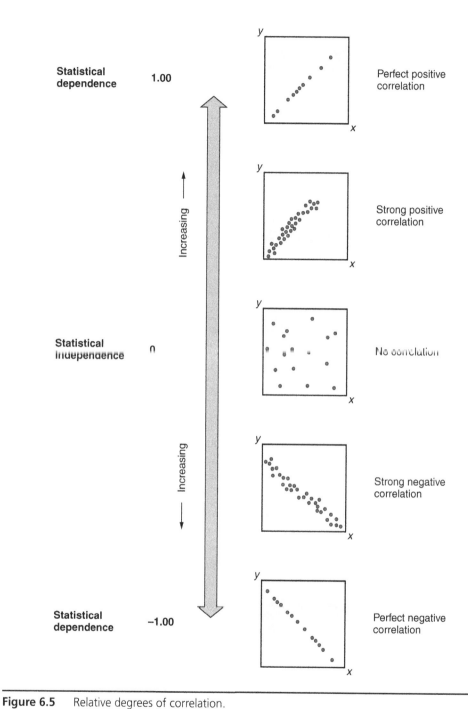

Figure 6.5   Relative degrees of correlation.

Source: M. A. Durivage, *Practical Engineering, Process, and Reliability Engineering Statistics* (Milwaukee: ASQ Quality Press, 2014). Used with permission.

where

Y = The measured value

X = The reference value

n = The number of reference parts

To calculate the coefficient of determination:

The correlation coefficient is squared (r^2)

where

r = Correlation coefficient

$r_{\alpha,df(n-2)}$ = Correlation value for a given α with ($n - 2$) degrees of freedom (see Appendix D, Critical Values of the Correlation Coefficient)

$$r = \frac{n \times \Sigma XY - \Sigma X \times \Sigma Y}{\sqrt{n \times \Sigma X^2 - (\Sigma X)^2} \times \sqrt{n \times \Sigma Y^2 - (\Sigma Y)^2}}$$

$$= \frac{7 \times 1789494 - 3492 \times 3266}{\sqrt{7 \times 1899812 - (3492)^2} \times \sqrt{7 \times 1686640 - (3266)^2}}$$

$$= 0.9996$$

$$r^2 = 0.9996^2 = 0.9992$$

The correlation coefficient is 0.9996, which indicates a strong positive relationship. The coefficient of determination r^2 is simply the correlation coefficient squared. In this case the coefficient of determination is 0.9992, indicating that 99.92% of the variation of the measured value (Y) is explained by the variation in the reference value (X).

Additionally, we wish to use the critical values of the correlation coefficient to test the relationship between X and Y variables with $\alpha = 0.05$. From the table, with $\alpha = 0.05$ (95%) with df($n - 2$) is 0.754. Since $r_{Calcualted}$ (0.9996) > $r_{Critical}$ (0.754) we are 95% confident there is a statistically significant relationship between the X (reference values) and Y (measured values).

6.4 LINEARITY TEST

An additional test for linearity uses the percentage points of Student's t-distribution. The following calculations are used to perform this test:

$$\left| t_{Calculated} \right| = \frac{|a|}{\left(\dfrac{s}{\sqrt{\Sigma(X - \bar{X})^2}} \right)}$$

$$s = \sqrt{\frac{\Sigma(Y^2 - b)\Sigma(Y - a)\Sigma(XY)}{n-2}}$$

where

Y = The measured value

a = Slope of the line

b = The y intercept

s = Standard deviation

X = The reference value

n = The number of reference parts

$t_{1-(\alpha/2),\,\text{df}\,(n-2)}$ = Appendix E, Student's t-Distribution

If $t_{\text{Calculated}}$ is less than t_{Critical}, the linearity of the device is acceptable.

$$s = \sqrt{\frac{\Sigma(Y^2 - b)\Sigma(Y - a)\Sigma(XY)}{n-2}}$$

$$= \sqrt{\frac{1686918.4 \times 3258.9 \times 1789494}{7-2}} = 44357052.1$$

$$\left| t_{\text{Calculated}} \right| = \frac{|a|}{\left(\dfrac{s}{\sqrt{\Sigma(X - \bar{X})^2}} \right)} = \frac{|1.015|}{\left(\dfrac{44357052.1}{\sqrt{157802.9}} \right)} = 0.000$$

For this example we will use an α of 0.05. Using Appendix E, Student's t-Distribution, for 1 – (α/2) with n – 2 degrees of freedom, the t-statistic is 2.571. Since $t_{\text{Calulated}}$ (0.000) is between t_{Critical} (±2.571), the linearity of the device is acceptable (Figure 6.6).

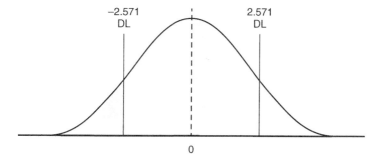

Figure 6.6   Decision limit for linearity.

6.5 BIAS TEST

To test the bias, use the following equation:

$$\left|t_{Calculated}\right| = \frac{|b|}{\left(\dfrac{\bar{X}^2}{\left[\sqrt{\dfrac{1}{n}+\Sigma\left(X-\bar{X}\right)^2}\right]}\right)s}$$

$$s = \sqrt{\frac{\Sigma\left(Y^2-b\right)\Sigma(Y-a)\Sigma(XY)}{n-2}}$$

where

Y = The measured value

a = Slope of the line

b = The Y intercept

X = The reference value

n = The number of reference parts

$t_{1-(\alpha/2),\,df\,(n-2)}$ = Appendix E, Student's t-Distribution

If $t_{Calulated}$ is less than $t_{Critical}$, the bias of the device is acceptable.

$$s = \sqrt{\frac{\Sigma\left(Y^2-b\right)\Sigma(Y-a)\Sigma(XY)}{n-2}}$$

$$= \sqrt{\frac{1686918.4\times3258.9\times1789494}{7-2}} = 44357052.1$$

$$\left|t_{Calculated}\right| = \frac{|b|}{\left(\dfrac{\bar{X}^2}{\left[\sqrt{\dfrac{1}{n}+\Sigma\left(X-\bar{X}\right)^2}\right]}\right)s} = \frac{|-39.769|}{\left(\dfrac{498.8^2}{\left[\sqrt{\dfrac{1}{7}+157802.9}\right]}\right)44357052.1} = 0.000$$

For this example we will use an α of 0.05. Using Appendix E, Student's t-Distribution for $1-(\alpha/2)$ with $n-2$ degrees of freedom, the t-statistic is 2.571. Since $t_{Calculated}$ (0.000) is between $t_{Critical}$ (±2.571), the bias of the device is acceptable (Figure 6.7).

Figure 6.8 is the plot depicting the bias and linearity for the example. The plot indicates nearly perfect bias and lineraity.

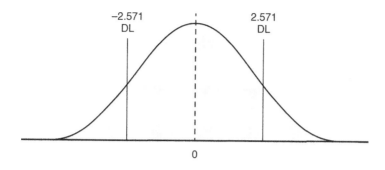

Figure 6.7 Decision limit for bias.

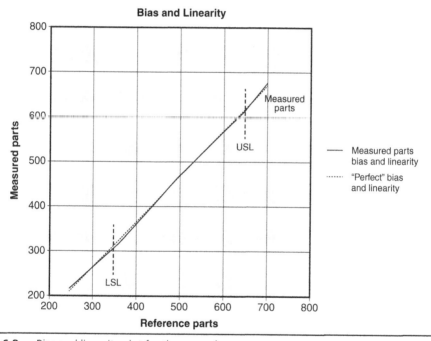

Figure 6.8 Bias and linearity plot for the example.

6.6 STABILITY

Stability is a measure of the decline in performance of the measuring device over time, usually due to wear or degradation. Analyzing the stability can help determine the calibration interval for the measuring device. Stability evaluates whether the degree of bias changes over time by using a control chart that uses the same reference part over time. It is recommended that the reference part, or *standard*, should be as close to the target value—which hopefully is also the process average—as possible. An $\bar{X}$ and R chart or an individuals and moving range (ImR) chart is typically used to evaluate gage stability. However, an ImR chart is usually sufficient. If the measurement system is not stable, gage R&R studies will not be valid over time. Either the actual measurement or the reference dimension minus the actual dimension can be used to construct the chart.

It is very important to maintain the integrity of the reference part. It must be not be subject to wear from the measuring device or deteriorate over time, which could alter its dimensions (that is, corrosion, erosion, and so on).

Analyzing the measuring device stability will use the same rules as for control charts. When a previously stable device shows signs of instability, it is an indication that it is time to recalibrate the measuring device.

6.7 CONTROL CHART INTERPRETATION

A process is said to be in control when the control chart does not indicate any special cause variation or out-of-control condition and contains only common causes of variation. *Special cause variation* is not anticipated and inherently unpredictable, whereas *common cause variation* is the natural variation of the process, sometimes referred to as the *noise* of the process. If the common cause variation is small, then a control chart can be used to monitor the process. See Figure 6.9 for a representation of stable (in control) and unstable (out of control) processes. If the common cause variation is too large, the process will need to be modified.

When a control chart indicates an out-of-control condition (a point outside the control limits or matching one or more of the criteria below), the assignable causes of variation must be identified and eliminated.

Improper control chart interpretation can lead to several problems, including blaming people for problems they can not control, spending time and money looking for problems that do not exist, spending time and money on process adjustments or new equipment that are not necessary, taking action where no action is warranted, and asking

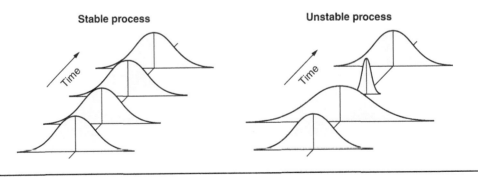

Figure 6.9   Stable and unstable variation.

Source: M. A. Durivage, *Practical Engineering, Process, and Reliability Engineering Statistics* (Milwaukee: ASQ Quality Press, 2014). Used with permission.

for worker-related improvements where process or equipment improvements need to be made first.

The following rules should be used to properly interpret control charts:

Rule 1—One point beyond the 3σ control limits

Rule 2—Eight or more points on one side of the centerline without crossing

Rule 3—Four out of five points in zone B or beyond

Rule 4—Six points or more in a row steadily increasing or decreasing

Rule 5—Two out of three points in zone A

Rule 6—14 points in a row alternating up and down

Rule 7—Any noticeable/predictable pattern, cycle, or trend

Please note that depending on the source, these rules can vary. See Figure 6.10 for control chart interpretation rules.

6.8 $\bar{X}$ AND R CONTROL CHARTS

$\bar{X}$ and R control charts assume a normal distribution and are usually used with a subgroup size of less than 10 (typically 3–5). A minimum of 25 subgroups is necessary to construct the chart.

$\bar{X}$ chart	R chart

$$\bar{X} = \frac{\Sigma X}{n} \text{ (subgroup)} \qquad\qquad R = X_h - X_l \text{ (subgroup)}$$

$$\bar{\bar{X}} = \frac{\Sigma \bar{X}}{k} \text{ (centerline)} \qquad\qquad \bar{R} = \frac{\Sigma R}{k} \text{ (centerline)}$$

$$\bar{X}\text{UCL} = \bar{\bar{X}} + A_2\bar{R} \qquad\qquad \bar{R}\text{UCL} = D_4\bar{R}$$

$$\bar{X}\text{LCL} = \bar{\bar{X}} - A_2 R \qquad\qquad \bar{R}\text{LCL} = D_3\bar{R}$$

where

n = Subgroup size

k = The number of subgroups

(See Appendix A for control chart constants.)

Example: A measurement system's stability is to be monitored with an $\bar{X}$ and R chart. Measurements are collected once a week at the end of the shift from a known reference part, which measures 500. The data collected have an $\bar{X}$ of 499.8 and an $\bar{R}$ of 16.6.

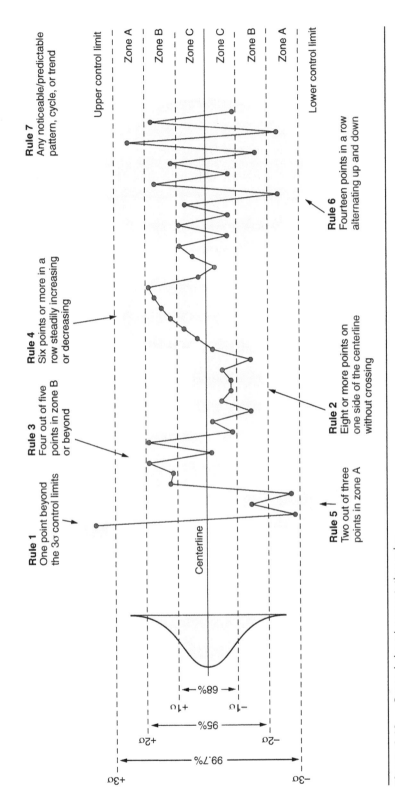

Figure 6.10 Control chart interpretation rules.
Source: M. A. Durivage, *Practical Engineering, Process, and Reliability Engineering Statistics* (Milwaukee: ASQ Quality Press, 2014). Used with permission.

Table 6.3   Data for $\bar{X}$ and R chart.

Subgroup	$\bar{X}$	R
1	504.7	7
2	493.7	5
3	493.7	6
4	502.0	18
5	495.7	18
6	502.7	26
7	495.0	4
8	492.3	21
9	494.7	32
10	499.7	27
11	505.3	11
12	503.7	20
13	500.7	14
14	495.7	14
15	509.3	23
16	502.3	12
17	497.0	16
18	501.3	29
19	500.7	19
20	500.3	33
21	498.0	15
22	507.3	21
23	504.3	5
24	496.7	10
25	498.7	10
Sum	12495.3	416
Average	499.8	16.6

Twenty-five subgroups of three samples are taken (Table 6.3). Calculate the centerlines and upper and lower control limits, and construct an $\bar{X}$ and R chart (Figure 6.11).

$$\bar{\bar{X}} = \frac{\Sigma \bar{X}}{k} = \frac{12495.3}{25} = 499.8$$

$$\bar{R} = \frac{\Sigma R}{k} = \frac{416}{25} = 16.6$$

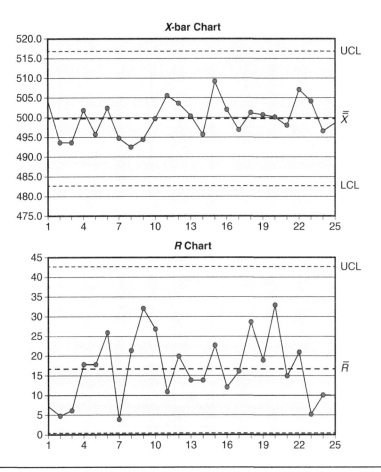

Figure 6.11 *X*-bar and *R* chart example.

$$\bar{X}\text{UCL} = \bar{\bar{X}} + A_2\bar{R} = 499.8 + 1.023 \times 16.6 = 516.8$$

$$\bar{X}\text{LCL} = \bar{\bar{X}} - A_2\bar{R} = 499.8 - 1.023 \times 16.6 = 482.8$$

$$\bar{R}\text{UCL} = D_4\bar{R} = 2.574 \times 16.6 = 42.7$$

$$\bar{R}\text{LCL} = D_3\bar{R} = 0 \times 16.6 = 0$$

A graphical review of the $\bar{X}$ and R chart in Figure 6.11 does not indicate the presence of any special cause variation, providing evidence that the gage (measuring system) is stable.

6.9 XmR (MOVING RANGE) CHARTS

XmR (moving range) control charts assume a normal distribution and are used with individual values. A minimum of 25 observations is necessary to construct the chart.

X chart	mR chart
X (individual observation)	$mR = \|X_2 - X_1\|, \|X_3 - X_2\|\ldots$
$\bar{X} = \dfrac{\Sigma X}{k}$ (centerline)	$\overline{mR} = \dfrac{\Sigma mR}{k-1}$ (centerline)
$UCL = \bar{X} + d_2 \times \overline{mR}$	$UCL = D_4 \times \overline{mR}$
$LCL = \bar{X} - d_2 \times \overline{mR}$	$LCL = 0$

(See Appendix A for control chart constants.)

where

k = The number of subgroups

Example: A measurement system's stability is to be monitored with an XmR chart. Measurements are collected once a week at the end of the shift from a known reference part, which measures 500. Twenty-five measurements are taken (Table 6.4). Calculate the centerlines and upper and lower control limits, and construct an XmR chart (Figure 6.12).

$$\bar{X} = \frac{\Sigma X}{k} = \frac{12511}{25} = 500.4$$

$$\overline{mR} = \frac{\Sigma mR}{k-1} = \frac{106}{25-1} = 4.4$$

$$UCL = \bar{X} + d_2 \times \overline{mR} = 500.4 + 1.128 \times 4.4 = 505.4$$

$$LCL = \bar{X} - d_2 \times \overline{mR} = 500.4 - 1.128 \times 4.4 = 495.4$$

$$UCL = D_4 \times \overline{mR} = 3.267 \times 4.4 = 14.4$$

$$LCL = 0$$

A graphical review of the XmR chart in Figure 6.12 indicates the presence of special cause variation, providing evidence that the gage (measuring system) is unstable. An investigation into the cause of the special cause variation should be conducted, and the special cause variation removed and the study reexecuted.

Table 6.4   Data for XmR chart.

Subgroup	X	mR
1	500	0
2	506	6
3	501	5
4	503	2
5	495	8
6	505	10
7	501	4
8	495	6
9	501	6
10	504	3
11	500	4
12	498	2
13	504	6
14	502	2
15	504	2
16	502	2
17	503	1
18	500	3
19	498	2
20	495	3
21	502	7
22	496	6
23	501	5
24	495	6
25	500	5
Sum	12511	106

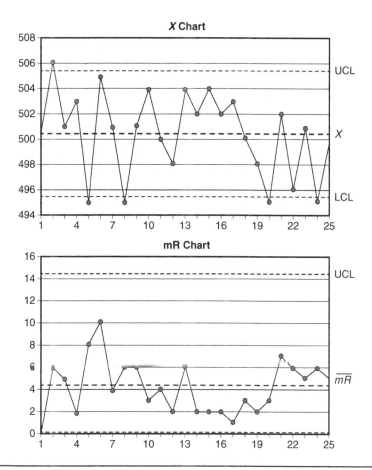

Figure 6.12   XmR chart example.

7

Measurement Uncertainty and Guard Banding

7.1 TYPE A AND TYPE B UNCERTAINTIES

A key component of gage R&R studies is recognizing and acknowledging the presence of type A and type B uncertainties. For a measurement systems analysis to be useful, one must identify the effects and, where possible, evaluate the measurement uncertainties. *Type A* uncertainties are those that can be calculated by statistical means, such as repeatability, reproducibility, accuracy, linearity, bias, and stability.

Type B uncertainties are uncertainties associated with measurement systems that can not be evaluated by statistical methods. Type B uncertainty is typically established by previous experience and does not rely on statistical calculations, or simply, is any uncertainty that is not type A (see Figure 7.1).

7.2 GUARD BANDING

Guard banding is the practice of utilizing the gage R&R results to reduce the range of acceptance to ensure that features are within the prescribed specifications. This is especially important with products that can have a detrimental effect on health and safety issues. Parts that fall within the guard banded (reject) areas do not necessarily need to

Type A uncertainties	Type B uncertainties
• Accuracy	• Published handbook values
• Bias	• Results from previous measurements
• Linearity	• Manufacturer's specification
• Stability	• Value of a certified reference
• Repeatability	• Instrument class
• Reproducibility	• Calibration certificate
	• Physical constants
	• Environmental effects
	• Reference standards

Figure 7.1   Type A and B measurement uncertainties.

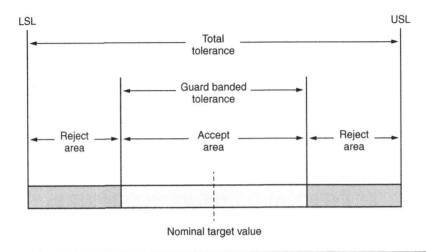

Figure 7.2   Guard banding.

be scrapped or reworked, but should receive further evaluation prior to final product disposition determination. Figure 7.2 depicts the concept of guard banding.

The formulas used to calculate the guard band are as follows:

$$GB_{TT} = TT - GB \times 2 \times TT$$

$$GB_{LSL} = LSL + GB \times TT$$

$$GB_{USL} = USL - GB \times TT$$

where

TT = Total tolerance

GB = From Appendix F (GRR%, threshold percentage)

LSL = Lower specification limit

USL = Upper specification limit

GRR = Percentage of the total tolerance

It is apparent that guard banding can consume a substantial portion of the allowable tolerance. There are three things that can be done to reduce the effects of guard banding:

1. Negotiate for a larger tolerance allowance.

2. Work to decrease the overall gage R&R (see Chapter 10).

3. Reduce the threshold percentage. This will, however, increase the risk of
    passing out-of-specification product.

	Good product	Defective product
Accepted by consumer	OK	Consumer's risk (type 2 or β risk)
Rejected by consumer	Producer's risk (type 1 or α risk)	OK

Figure 7.3   Consumer's and producer's risk.

Additionally, reducing the process variation and/or centering the process will be beneficial.

To select the proper threshold percentage, the consumer's and producer's risk must be evaluated. *Consumer's risk* is the probability that a defective product will be accepted by the customer. *Producer's risk* is the probability that a good product will be rejected by the customer (see Figure 7.3). Appendix F provides decreasing levels of risk acceptance for 70%, 80%, 90%, 95%, 99%, and 100% guard banding thresholds. Each manufacturer should select the threshold that balances the risks and revenue associated with the product.

7.3 GUARD BANDING USING THE TRADITIONAL GAGE R&R EXAMPLE

From the traditional R&R study example in Section 4.2, $\sigma_{RR} = 8.45$ with the gage R&R found to be 16.73%, which is considered marginally acceptable. The acceptable specification for the feature is USL 650 – LSL 350 (total tolerance is 300). The process has a historical process standard deviation of 50. Due to the risk associated with this part, a 95% threshold percentage will be used. Figure 7.4 shows the effects of guard banding.

$$GB_{TT} = TT - GB \times 2 \times TT = 300 - 0.081 \times 2 \times 300 = 251.4$$

$$GB_{LSL} = LSL + GB \times TT = 350 - 0.081 \times 300 = 374.3$$

$$GB_{USL} = USL - GB \times TT = 650 - 0.081 \times 300 = 625.7$$

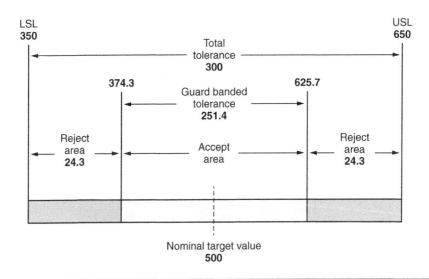

Figure 7.4 Traditional gage R&R guard banding results.

7.4 GUARD BANDING USING THE ANOVA GAGE R&R EXAMPLE

From the ANOVA R&R study example in Section 5.2, $\sigma_{RR} = 10.77$ with the gage R&R found to be 21.54%, which is considered marginally acceptable. The acceptable specification for the feature is USL 650 – LSL 350 (total tolerance is 300). The process has a historical process standard deviation of 50. Due to the risk associated with this part, a 90% threshold percentage will be used. Figure 7.5 shows the effects of guard banding in ANOVA gage R&R.

$$GB_{TT} = TT - GB \times 2 \times TT = 300 - 0.099 \times 2 \times 300 = 240.6$$

$$GB_{LSL} = LSL + GB \times TT = 350 - 0.099 \times 300 = 379.7$$

$$GB_{USL} = USL - GB \times TT = 650 - 0.099 \times 300 = 620.3$$

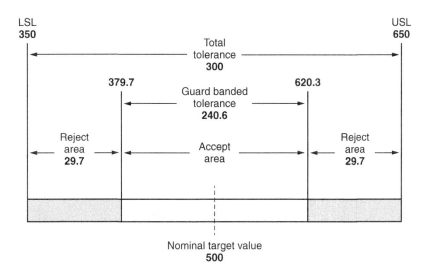

Figure 7.5   ANOVA gage R&R guard banding results.

8

Process and Measurement Capability Indices

There are two common measurement capability indices: MCI_1 and MCI_2. MCI_1 uses the process standard deviation (σ) and MCI_2 uses the feature tolerance to calculate the measurement capability index. Process capability is defined by comparing the 6σ interval of a statistically stable process to the specification range or tolerance. An index of this capability is

$$C_p = \frac{USL - LSL}{6\sigma_{Process}}$$

where

USL = Upper specification limit

LSL = Lower specification limit

USL and LSL refer to the upper and lower specification limits, respectively, and $\sigma_{Process}$ refers to the process standard deviation. This assesses variation observed in the process, and is an indicator of what the process could do if properly centered. A similar and more pertinent index, C_{pk}, indicates the capability of the process as it is currently centered. Since we are concerned with the spread in the process and not the average, C_p is the index to compare:

$$\sigma^2_{Observed} = \sigma^2_{Actual} + \sigma^2_{GRR}$$

where

$\sigma^2_{Observed}$ = Observed variation

σ^2_{Actual} = Actual variation

σ^2_{GRR} = Measurement system variation

8.1 MCI₁—MEASUREMENT CAPABILITY INDEX AS A PERCENTAGE OF PROCESS VARIATION

$$MCI_1 = \frac{\sigma_{GRR}}{\sigma_{Process}}$$

It is important to note that σ should be estimated from a process control range chart, using

$$\sigma_{\text{Process}} = \frac{\bar{R}}{d_2}$$

where

d_2 = Number of trials (See Appendix A, Control Chart Constants)

Some references use the variation in the samples of the study to estimate this variation. Such a procedure is not recommended since it is difficult to appropriately represent process variation with the small samples used in a measurement study. Samples are better chosen to represent the range of measurements anticipated rather than trying to select them to define a large population.

MCI_1 is the most commonly used index since it indicates, as shown in Figure 8.1, the comparative size of the distribution of the measurement system to that of the process being measured. Since the measured process variation is a combination of the true process variation and the measurement variation, this index indicates the degree of distortion due to measurement in reporting the process variation. This index is independent of the specifications and indicates the clarity with which the process can be viewed. When a one-sided specification is used, it is the only index that can be used without artificially creating a specification.

MCI_1 has the disadvantage of the component values not being additive. That is, the index for repeatability plus that of reproducibility does not equal the index for R&R. (This is a result of using the sigmas rather than the squares of the sigmas.) Despite this drawback, this index is clearly communicated and provides a good indicator of the adequacy of the measurement system. The criteria for assessment of this index are shown in Table 8.1.

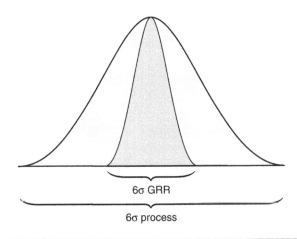

6σ GRR

6σ process

Figure 8.1   Gage R&R as a proportion of process variation.

Table 8.1	Gage acceptability criteria for the MCI_1 index.	
Gage R&R	**Acceptance**
< 10%	Acceptable
10%–30%	Marginally acceptable
> 30%	Unacceptable

An "unacceptable" rating implies that measurement distorts the apparent process variation, and there is a need to improve the measurement system before one can address the production process. This result should also be viewed in conjunction with the process capability index as represented by the process C_p, the indicator of the adequacy of process spread. An "unacceptable" MCI_1 is an opportunity to improve; however, if the C_p is adequate, improving measurement may not be an immediate priority. A poor index means that improved measurement performance will improve the observed process capability; a good index means there is little benefit in further reducing the measurement variation. This is the preferred index since it is not dependent on specifications and its criteria can be defined statistically.

8.2 MCI₂—MEASUREMENT CAPABILITY INDEX AS A PERCENTAGE OF PROCESS SPECIFICATIONS

$$MCI_2 = \frac{6\sigma_{GRR}}{USL - LSL}$$

where

USL = Upper specification limit

LSL = Lower specification limit

This index, illustrated in Figure 8.2, shows the size of the measurement variation compared to the tolerance (specification) range. This index remains the easiest to explain, and still has value in indicating the status of the measurement variation with respect to the process specifications being applied. The problem with this index is that specifications are not necessarily set reasonably nor are they consistent from one application to another. Specifications that are either too generous or too tight may lead to misleading interpretations and comparisons of measurement systems. This index shows the ability to classify product against the specifications, while index MCI_1 indicates the distortion in the process variation due to measurement. These are two different questions. The utility of MCI_2 is illustrated in Figure 8.3.

Figure 8.3 illustrates the range of possible values that might be reported for an actual value occurring near a spec limit. The larger the R&R, the greater is the risk of misclassification.

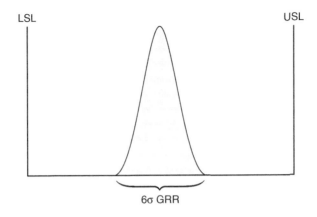

Figure 8.2 Gage R&R as a proportion of the tolerance.

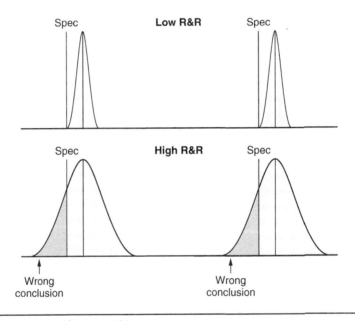

Figure 8.3 Errors caused by gage R&R.

The customary criteria for assessment of the index are similar to MCI_1 (see Table 8.2).

These criteria, while common practice, are not statistically based. While the index is a very descriptive indicator, its meaning is dependent on the specifications.

As with MCI_1, the index is applied to R&R initially and to the components only if the R&R is not acceptable. The index should be interpreted in conjunction with the process capability index (C_p) to better establish the priority for measurement improvement.

If the variable being measured has only a single specification, the tolerance can not be defined and this index can not be used. The tolerance is based on product or process

Table 8.2 Gage acceptability criteria for the MCI$_2$ index.

Gage R&R	Acceptance
< 20%	Acceptable
20%–30%	Marginally acceptable
> 30%	Unacceptable

specifications. If the tolerance used is the manufacturer's specification for the measurement device, the interpretation of the R&R results is quite different.

If only one index is used, MCI$_1$ is preferred. It is more meaningful statistically, is consistent in its interpretation, and is independent of the specifications. However, remember that each index is answering a different question: MCI$_1$ looks at how measurement contributes to the observed process variation; MCI$_2$ looks to see how well one can interpret specifications for given measurement variation. Note that a single indicator is not sufficient to completely describe the status of the measurement system as part of the production process. It would be preferable to include the process C$_p$ with a measurement index to put the measurement process in proper context for assigning priority. (C$_p$ is used since it refers to the spread capability of the production process. The C$_{pk}$ includes the targeting of the process average, something outside the description of variation.) If the C$_p$ is good (>1.0), a poor measurement process needs improvement, but may not be an immediate priority.

8.3 GAGE R&R AND PROCESS CAPABILITY

Obviously, any improvement (reduction) in the gage R&R variation will also reduce the observed process variation, increasing the process capability index and reducing the measurement capability. Figure 8.4 shows the degree of distortion of the actual process C$_p$ due to the amount of measurement variation shown by MCI$_1$, using the process sigma. A similar graph can be generated for MCI$_2$, using specifications as the reference.

Several observations are apparent from a study of the graphs in Figures 8.4 and 8.5:

1. Impact of gage R&R variation in either case is minor if the index is less than .3, or 30%.

2. The MCI$_1$ index is more robust than MCI$_2$.

3. At first, it may be surprising that the gage R&R results have a negligible effect on actual C$_p$ at the low values of observed C$_p$. This indicates that the overwhelming problem in such cases is improvement of the process. Improvement to the measurement system, while necessary, will not correct an obviously incapable process.

4. Gage R&R becomes more influential as the observed process capability increases to at least marginal levels.

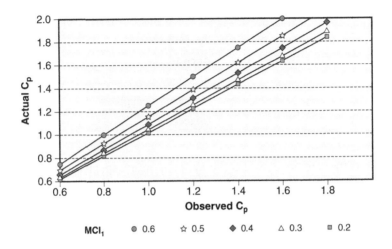

Figure 8.4   Distortion of C_p for MCI_1.

Source: L. B. Barrentine, *Concepts for R&R Studies*, 2nd ed. (Milwaukee: ASQ Quality Press, 2003). Used with permission.

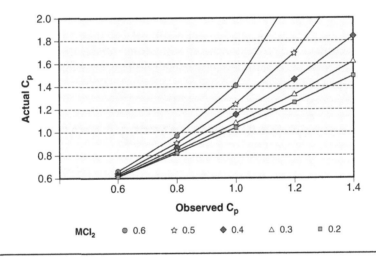

Figure 8.5   Distortion of C_p for MCI_2.

Source: L. B. Barrentine, *Concepts for R&R Studies*, 2nd ed. (Milwaukee: ASQ Quality Press, 2003). Used with permission.

8.4 HOW THE INDICES RELATE TO ONE ANOTHER AND TO C_p

The three indices (MCI_1, MCI_2, and C_p) are completely linked. Any two of these will completely specify the third. This supports the point that a single measurement capability index is not sufficient to fully define the measurement/process situation, while any two of these provide a complete picture of measurement and process. Figure 8.6 displays the interrelation of the three indices.

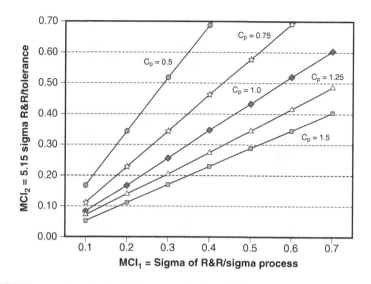

Figure 8.6   Relationship of C_p and measurement capability indices.
Source: L. B. Barrentine, *Concepts for R&R Studies*, 2nd ed. (Milwaukee: ASQ Quality Press, 2003). Used with permission.

A review of Figure 8.6 reveals:

1. The two measurement capability indices used together define process capability. One index and the C_p will define the second index.

2. A full appreciation of the process status is best achieved by a measurement index *and* C_p.

3. A good C_p can only be achieved with poor measurement capability (using MCI_1) when the actual process variation is relatively small and/or the specifications are wide (reflected by a small MCI_2 index).

4. The two measurement capability indices described here answer two different questions about the measurement process. Neither is sufficient to indicate the priority and impact of measurement on a specific production process. Full comprehension requires an MCI with the C_p.

5. MCI_1 will *usually* be a more stringent requirement than MCI_2. That is, in the range of marginal C_p or better, the criteria for MCI_2 are more forgiving than those of MCI_1.

8.5 RELATIONSHIP BETWEEN PROCESS CAPABILITY AND MEASUREMENT CAPABILITY INDICES

The two measurement capability indices (MCI_1 and MCI_2) and process capability (as indicated by C_p) are related such that any two of these indices will specify the third. (C_p is used since it specifies the process spread.)

$$MCI_1 = \frac{\sigma_{GRR}}{\sigma_{Process}} ; MCI_2 = \frac{6\sigma_{GRR}}{USL - LSL} ; C_P = \frac{USL - LSL}{6\sigma_{Process}}$$

From the first two equations,

$$\sigma_{Process} = USL - LSL = \frac{6\sigma_{GRR}}{MCI_2}$$

Then, substituting these last two expressions into the C_p formula,

$$C_P = \frac{USL - LSL}{6\sigma_{Process}} = \frac{\frac{6\sigma_{GRR}}{MCI_2}}{6 \times \left(\frac{\sigma_{GRR}}{MCI_1}\right)} = \frac{6 \times MCI_1}{6 \times MCI_2} = \frac{MCI_1}{MCI_2}$$

Figure 8.7 plots C_p's for various values of the two measurement capability indices. Review of these plots shows that a good C_p is possible with a poor MCI only if there is a generous specification and/or the gage R&R variation (σ_{GRR}) is a dominant part of the observed variation ($\sigma_{Process}$). The primary value of these relationships is that they validate the advantage of using C_p with a measurement index to better understand the total process and measurement situation.

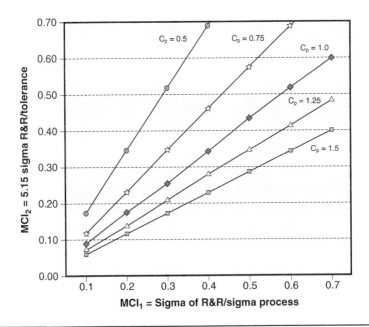

Figure 8.7 C_p contours for MCI_1 and MCI_2.
Source: L. B. Barrentine, *Concepts for R&R Studies*, 2nd ed. (Milwaukee: ASQ Quality Press, 2003). Used with permission.

8.6 THE EFFECT OF GAGE R&R ON PROCESS CAPABILITY

The improvement possible in process capability resulting from improvement in R&R can be calculated using the formula

$$\sigma^2_{Observed} = \sigma^2_{Actual} + \sigma^2_{GRR}$$

where

$\sigma^2_{Observed}$ = Observed variation

σ^2_{Actual} = Actual variation

σ^2_{GRR} = Measurement system variation

Given the values of $\sigma_{Observed}$ and σ_{GRR}, σ_{Actual} can be calculated. As reduced values of σ_{GRR} are estimated, the reduced value of $\sigma_{Observed}$ can be estimated. Then the improved measurement capability index can be calculated by either of the two indices. This can also be expedited by the following derivations.

MCI₁ (in Proportions)

$$MCI_1 = \frac{\sigma_{GRR}}{\sigma_{Process}}$$

Based on the equation above, $\sigma^2_{Part} = \sigma^2_{Process} - \sigma^2_{GRR}$

$$C_{p-Observed} = \frac{USL - LSL}{6\sigma_{Observed}} \quad \text{and} \quad C_{p-Actual} = \frac{USL - LSL}{6\sigma_{Actual}}$$

$$\text{Then, } C_{p-Actual} = \frac{USL - LSL}{6\sqrt{\sigma^2_{Observed} - \sigma^2_{GRR}}} = \frac{USL - LSL}{6\sigma_{Observed}\sqrt{1 - \frac{\sigma^2_{GRR}}{\sigma^2_{Observed}}}} = \frac{C_{p-Observed}}{\sqrt{1 - \frac{\sigma^2_{GRR}}{\sigma^2_{Observed}}}}$$

$$\text{Resulting in } C_{p-Actual} = \frac{C_{p-Observed}}{\sqrt{1 - (MCI_1)^2}}$$

This is the equation used to develop Figure 8.4 showing the effect of MCI_1 on C_p.

MCI₂ (in Proportions)

$$MCI_2 = \frac{6\sigma_{GRR}}{USL - LSL} \quad \text{and} \quad C_{p-Observed} = \frac{USL - LSL}{6\sigma_{Observed}}$$

$$\text{Then, } \sigma_{\text{Observed}} = \frac{\text{USL} - \text{LSL}}{6C_{p-\text{Actual}}}$$

$$\sigma^2_{\text{Actual}} = \left(\frac{\text{USL} - \text{LSL}}{6C_{p-\text{Observed}}}\right)^2 - \sigma^2_{\text{GRR}}$$

$$C_{p-\text{Actual}} = \frac{\text{USL} - \text{LSL}}{6\sigma_{\text{Actual}}} = \frac{\text{USL} - \text{LSL}}{6\sqrt{\left(\dfrac{\text{USL} - \text{LSL}}{6C_{p-\text{Observed}}}\right)^2 - \sigma^2_{\text{GRR}}}}$$

$$C_{p-\text{Actual}} = \frac{1}{6\sqrt{\left(\dfrac{1}{6C_{p-\text{Observed}}}\right)^2 - \left(\dfrac{\sigma_{\text{GRR}}}{\text{USL} - \text{LSL}}\right)^2}}$$

$$C_{p-\text{Actual}} = \frac{1}{6\sqrt{\left(\dfrac{1}{6C_{p-\text{Observed}}}\right)^2 - \left(\dfrac{\text{MCI}_2}{6}\right)^2}}$$

This expression was used to generate Figure 8.5. Note that some combinations are not possible.

8.7 CONFIDENCE LEVELS IN ESTIMATING STANDARD DEVIATIONS

The gage R&R process is one of estimating standard deviations. Appendix B allows assurance that there will be at least 14 degrees of freedom in the estimation of repeatability. Typical statistical analysis defines degrees of freedom as df = $k(n - 1)$, where n is the number of observations of each of k samples used to make the estimate. In gage R&R studies using the range estimates, the degrees of freedom will be slightly less than this because of the small number of samples and/or the small sample sizes.

Duncan C. McCune prepared a chart that related sample size to precision of estimates of standard deviations. The chart is not exact for gage R&R estimates, but it is close enough to indicate the relative precision of our results if we approximate degrees of freedom by df = $.9k(n - 1)$, where k is the number of parts and n is the number of trials. Figure 8.8 uses the chi-square relationship:

$$\chi^2_{a,d,f} = \frac{(\text{df})s^2}{\sigma^2}$$

To estimate the curves, it is important to note that:

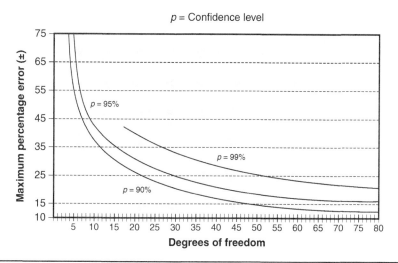

p = Confidence level

Figure 8.8   Precision in estimating the standard deviation as a function of degrees of freedom.
Source: L. B. Barrentine, *Concepts for R&R Studies*, 2nd ed. (Milwaukee: ASQ Quality Press, 2003).
Used with permission.

1. Reproducibility typically has 1, 2, or 3 degrees of freedom (one less than the number of appraisers). Such small degrees of freedom imply that extreme variability is possible in that estimate.

2. Repeatability should have a minimum of 14 degrees of freedom. Note that there is still a potential error of as much as 30 percent at the 90 percent confidence level and 37 percent at the 95 percent confidence level.

An R&R study should not be run once and forgotten. Such studies must be performed regularly, and records kept on corrective actions to monitor the performance over time. The frequency of reexecuting the gage R&R study depends on several factors, including but not limited to:

- A change in the gage
- A change in the specification/feature
- An increase in the amount of rejected product
- An increase in customer complaints
- The effect of the feature on health and/or safety
- A new application for the gage

8.8 TRADITIONAL R&R STUDY EXAMPLE

From the traditional R&R study example in Section 4.2, $\sigma_{GRR} = 8.45$, with the gage R&R found to be 16.73%, which is considered marginally acceptable. The acceptable specification for the feature is USL 650 – LSL 350 (total tolerance is 300). The process has a historical process standard deviation of 50. Using this information, calculate MCI_1 and MCI_2 using the following equations:

$$C_p = \frac{USL - LSL}{6\sigma_{Process}} = \frac{650 - 350}{6 \times 50} = 1.00$$

$$MCI_1 = \frac{\sigma_{GRR}}{\sigma_{Process}} = \frac{8.45}{50} = 0.17$$

$$MCI_2 = \frac{6\sigma_{GRR}}{USL - LSL} = \frac{6 \times 8.45}{650 - 350} = 0.17 \text{ or } 17\%$$

To verify the relationships:

$$C_p = \frac{MCI_1}{MCI_2} = \frac{0.17}{0.17} = 1.0$$

Note: MCI_1 and MCI_2 will not always be the same value.

8.9 ANOVA GAGE R&R STUDY EXAMPLE

From the ANOVA R&R study example in Section 5.2, $\sigma_{GRR} = 10.77$ with the gage R&R found to be 21.54%, which is considered marginally acceptable. The acceptable specification for the feature is USL 650 – LSL 350 (total tolerance is 300). The process has a historical process standard deviation of 50. Using this information, calculate MCI_1 and MCI_2 using the following equations:

$$C_p = \frac{USL - LSL}{6\sigma_{Process}} = \frac{650 - 350}{6 \times 50} = 1.00$$

$$MCI_1 = \frac{\sigma_{GRR}}{\sigma_{Process}} = \frac{10.77}{50} = 0.22$$

$$MCI_2 = \frac{6\sigma_{GRR}}{USL - LSL} = \frac{6 \times 10.77}{650 - 350} = 0.22 \text{ or } 22\%$$

To verify the relationships:

$$C_p = \frac{MCI_1}{MCI_2} = \frac{0.22}{0.22} = 1.0$$

Note: MCI_1 and MCI_2 will not always be the same value.

9

Performing an Attribute Gage R&R Study

Performing attribute gage R&R studies provides a unique set of challenges when compared to studies using variable data. With variables measurements, the degree of conformity or nonconformity can be qualified with a physical measurement. Attribute assessments either accept or reject a part, without any indication of *how* good or bad the part actually is—only that it is good or bad. Because of pass/fail or good/bad (binary) data, there is less statistically known about the process/parts being inspected.

There are two basic approaches to conducting attribute gage R&R studies. The first approach uses known reference parts that represent the full range of variation of what is considered good or bad. To fully challenge the robustness and the ability of the measurement system, it is important to select some parts that are marginally considered good and marginally considered bad.

The other approach uses multiple operators without a standard to determine whether a part is acceptable or unacceptable. As with the above approach that uses a standard or reference parts, the study should be conducted with parts that represent the full range of variation.

As with gage R&R studies with variable data, it is extremely important to ensure that the gage is properly calibrated prior to use in the study. An additional consideration with attribute gage R&R studies is to ensure that the conditions of the study are well defined. Considerations for appraiser vision, lighting, and distance can have a significant impact when performing visual inspections for cosmetic defects. When given the opportunity, it is usually beneficial to utilize variable data to perform a gage R&R study because more statistical information can be generated to better characterize the measurement system.

9.1 THE SHORT-FORM ATTRIBUTE GAGE R&R STUDY

The *short-form attribute R&R study* is a simple and straightforward method for assessing the effectiveness of a measurement system. This method requires 20 parts, two appraisers, and two trials (see Figure 9.1). To fully challenge the robustness and the ability of the measurement system it is important to select some parts that are marginally considered good and marginally considered bad (see Figure 9.2). The study is deemed successful if all four assessments for each part agree.

	Appraiser A		Appraiser B	
Part	Trial 1	Trial 2	Trial 1	Trial 2
1				
2				
3				
4				
5				
6				
7				
8				
9				
10				
11				
12				
13				
14				
15				
16				
17				
18				
19				
20				

Figure 9.1   Short-form attribute R&R study template.

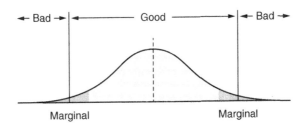

Figure 9.2   Sample selection distribution.

The Short-Form Attribute R&R Study Process

1. Determine the number of parts, trials, and appraisers necessary to conduct the study using a risk-based approach. To fully challenge the robustness

and the ability of the measurement system, it is important to select some parts that are marginally considered good and marginally considered bad.

2. Establish acceptability criteria based on risk.

3. Allow sufficient time for environmental stabilization of the parts and gage if applicable.

4. Verify the calibration status of the gage if applicable.

5. Ensure that each appraiser is properly trained and has the necessary competence to perform the study.

6. Collect the data and complete the short-form attribute R&R study template as shown in Figure 9.1.

7. Verify the results for each part, trial, and appraiser by circling any differences on the template.

8. Analyze the results and develop follow-up action as necessary. The study is deemed successful if all measurements agree with the standard. If there are any discrepancies, an alternative measurement system should be considered.

9. Document the reevaluation criteria and interval.

Example: To verify the presence of a feature on a part, a short-form attribute R&R study will be performed using 20 parts, two appraisers, and two trials. The measurement system will be acceptable if all four assessments for each part agree. The completed assessment is shown in Figure 9.3.

The measurement system is deemed adequate because all four assessments for each part agree.

9.2 THE SHORT-FORM ATTRIBUTE R&R STUDY WITH STANDARDS

The *short-form attribute R&R study with standards* is a method for assessing the effectiveness of a measurement system. This method requires 20 parts, two appraisers, and two trials (see Figure 9.4) that are compared to set of known reference parts (standards). To fully challenge the robustness and the ability of the measurement system, it is important to select some parts that are marginally considered good and marginally considered bad. If the individual appraiser score is greater than 90%, the results for the appraiser are considered acceptable (see Table 9.1). If the score is less than 90%, depending on the level of risk, the appraiser should be retrained, and the study for the appraiser that failed should be repeated. There may be cases in which there are health and safety concerns when the acceptable percentage should be raised or lowered based on risk acceptance. Additional consideration should be given to maintenance of the standards so that additional operators can be properly trained and documented.

Part	Appraiser A		Appraiser B	
	Trial 1	Trial 2	Trial 1	Trial 2
1	P	P	P	P
2	P	P	P	P
3	F	F	F	F
4	P	P	P	P
5	F	F	F	F
6	P	P	P	P
7	P	P	P	P
8	P	P	P	P
9	P	P	P	P
10	P	P	P	P
11	F	F	F	F
12	P	P	P	P
13	P	P	P	P
14	P	P	P	P
15	P	P	P	P
16	P	P	P	P
17	F	F	F	F
18	F	F	F	F
19	P	P	P	P
20	F	F	F	F

Figure 9.3   Completed short-form attribute R&R study.

The Short-Form Attribute R&R Study with Standards Process

1. Determine the number of parts, trials, and appraisers necessary to conduct the study using a risk-based approach. To fully challenge the robustness and the ability of the measurement system, it is important to select some parts that are marginally considered good and marginally considered bad.

2. Establish acceptability criteria based on risk.

3. Allow sufficient time for environmental stabilization of the parts and gage if applicable.

4. Verify the calibration status of the gage if applicable.

5. Ensure that each appraiser is properly trained and has the necessary competence to perform the study.

6. Collect the data and complete the short-form attribute R&R study with standards template as shown in Figure 9.4.

Part	Standard	Appraiser A		Appraiser B	
		Trial 1	Trial 2	Trial 1	Trial 2
1					
2					
3					
4					
5					
6					
7					
8					
9					
10					
11					
12					
13					
14					
15					
16					
17					
18					
19					
20					
Appraiser score					

Figure 9.4   Short-form attribute R&R study with standards template.

Table 9.1   Gage acceptability criteria.

Agreement	Acceptance
> 90%	Acceptable
90%–80%	Marginally acceptable
< 80%	Unacceptable

7. Verify the results for each part, trial, and appraiser by circling any measurement that does not agree with the standard. Calculate the percentage agreement for each appraiser with the formulas provided.

8. Analyze the results using the gage acceptability criteria provided in Table 9.1. Develop follow-up actions as necessary.

9. Document the reevaluation criteria and interval.

To calculate the appraiser percentage, use the following formula:

$$\text{Agreement } \% = \left(1 - \frac{r}{n \times t}\right) \times 100$$

where

  r = The number of disagreements

  n = Number of samples

  t = Number of trials

Example: To verify the presence of a feature on a part, a short-form attribute R&R study will be performed using 20 parts, two appraisers, and two trials. The measurement system will be acceptable if all four assessments for each part agree. The completed assessment is shown in Figure 9.5.

Part	Standard	Appraiser A		Appraiser B	
		Trial 1	Trial 2	Trial 1	Trial 2
1	P	F	P	P	P
2	P	P	P	F	P
3	F	F	F	F	F
4	P	P	P	P	P
5	F	P	F	F	F
6	P	P	P	P	P
7	P	P	P	P	P
8	P	P	F	P	P
9	P	P	P	P	P
10	P	P	P	F	F
11	F	F	F	F	F
12	P	P	P	F	P
13	P	P	P	F	P
14	P	P	P	P	P
15	P	P	P	P	F
16	P	P	P	P	P
17	F	F	F	F	F
18	F	F	F	P	F
19	P	P	P	P	P
20	F	F	F	F	F
Appraiser score		92.5%		82.5%	

Figure 9.5   Completed short-form attribute R&R study with standards.

For appraiser A:

$$\text{Agreement } \% = \left(1 - \frac{r}{n \times t}\right) \times 100 = \left(1 - \frac{3}{20 \times 2}\right) \times 100 = 92.5\%$$

For appraiser B:

$$\text{Agreement } \% = \left(1 - \frac{r}{n \times t}\right) \times 100 = \left(1 - \frac{7}{20 \times 2}\right) \times 100 = 82.5\%$$

Appraiser A has a score of 92.5% agreement with the standard and is deemed to be acceptable. Appraiser B has a score of 82.5% agreement with the standard and is deemed to be marginally acceptable. Appraiser B should be retrained and their portion of the study reexecuted.

9.3 ATTRIBUTE R&R STUDY WITH STANDARDS

There are times when the percentage of agreement does not provide enough discrimination to determine the suitability of the measurement system. The method presented here will assess the overall percentage of agreement as well as the leak rate and false alarms. A leak rate happens when a bad part is assessed as good (consumer's, type 2, or β risk). A false alarm is when a good part is assessed as bad (producer's, type 1, or α risk). Table 9.2 provides attribute R&R study with standards acceptability levels. The template is similar to the one used for the short-form attribute R&R study with standards with the exception of an added section to record the false alarm rate and the leak rate (see Figure 9.6).

The Attribute R&R Study with Standards Process

1. Determine the number of parts, trials, and appraisers necessary to conduct the study using a risk-based approach. To fully challenge the robustness and the ability of the measurement system, it is important to select some parts that are marginally considered good and marginally considered bad.

Table 9.2   Attribute R&R study with standards acceptability table.

	Acceptable	Marginally acceptable	Unacceptable
Agreement	> 90%	80–90%	< 80%
False alarm rate	< 5%	5–10%	> 10%
Leak rate	< 2%	2–5%	> 5%

Source: W. D. Mawby, *Make Your Destructive, Dynamic, and Attribute Measurement System Work for You* (Milwaukee: ASQ Quality Press, 2003). Used with permission.

Part	Standard	Appraiser A		Appraiser B	
		Trial 1	Trial 2	Trial 1	Trial 2
1					
2					
3					
4					
5					
6					
7					
8					
9					
10					
11					
12					
13					
14					
15					
16					
17					
18					
19					
20					
Agreement					
False alarm rate					
Leak rate					

Figure 9.6   Attribute R&R study with standards template.

2. Establish acceptability criteria based on risk.

3. Allow sufficient time for environmental stabilization of the parts and gage if applicable.

4. Verify the calibration status of the gage if applicable.

5. Ensure that each appraiser is properly trained and has the necessary competence to perform the study.

6. Collect the data and complete the attribute R&R study with standards template as shown in Figure 9.6.

7. Verify the results for each part, trial, and appraiser by circling any measurements that do not agree with the standard. Calculate the percentage agreement, false alarm rate, and leak rate with the formulas provided.

8. Analyze the results using the gage acceptability criteria provided in Table 9.2. Develop follow-up actions as necessary.

9. Document the reevaluation criteria and interval.

To calculate the appraiser percentage, use the following formula:

$$\text{Agreement } \% = \left(1 - \frac{r}{n \times t}\right) \times 100$$

$$\text{False alarm rate} = \frac{f}{n \times t} \times 100$$

$$\text{Leak rate} = \frac{l}{n \times t} \times 100$$

$$\text{Bias} = \frac{\text{False alarm rate}}{\text{Leak rate}}$$

(this is a relative measurement for a means of comparison)

where

r = The number of disagreements

f = The number of false alarms

l = The number of leaks

n = Number of samples

t = Number of trials

Example: To verify the presence of a feature on a part, an attribute R&R study with standards will be performed using 20 parts, two appraisers, and two trials. The completed assessment is shown in Figure 9.7.

For appraiser A:

$$\text{Agreement } \% = \left(1 - \frac{r}{n \times t}\right) \times 100 - \left(1 - \frac{3}{20 \times 2}\right) \times 100 = 92.5\%$$

$$\text{False alarm rate} = \frac{f}{n \times t} \times 100 = \frac{2}{20 \times 2} \times 100 = 5\%$$

$$\text{Leak rate} = \frac{l}{n \times t} \times 100 = \frac{1}{20 \times 2} \times 100 = 2.5\%$$

$$\text{Bias} = \frac{\text{False alarm rate}}{\text{Leak rate}} = \frac{5\%}{2.5\%} = 2.0$$

Part	Standard	Appraiser A		Appraiser B	
		Trial 1	Trial 2	Trial 1	Trial 2
1	P	(F)	P	P	P
2	P	P	P	(F)	P
3	F	F	F	F	F
4	P	P	P	P	P
5	F	(P)	F	F	F
6	P	P	P	P	P
7	P	P	P	P	P
8	P	P	(F)	P	P
9	P	P	P	P	P
10	P	P	P	(F)	(F)
11	F	F	F	F	F
12	P	P	P	(F)	P
13	P	P	P	(F)	P
14	P	P	P	P	P
15	P	P	P	P	(F)
16	P	P	P	P	P
17	F	F	F	F	F
18	F	F	F	(P)	F
19	P	P	P	P	P
20	F	F	F	F	F
Agreement		92.5%		82.5%	
False alarm rate		5%		12.5%	
Leak rate		2.5%		5%	

Figure 9.7   Attribute R&R study with standards results table.

For appraiser B:

$$\text{Agreement } \% = \left(1 - \frac{r}{n \times t}\right) \times 100 = \left(1 - \frac{7}{20 \times 2}\right) \times 100 = 82.5\%$$

$$\text{False alarm rate} = \frac{f}{n \times t} \times 100 = \frac{5}{20 \times 2} \times 100 = 12.5\%$$

$$\text{Leak rate} = \frac{l}{n \times t} \times 100 = \frac{2}{20 \times 2} \times 100 = 5\%$$

$$\text{Bias} = \frac{\text{False alarm rate}}{\text{Leak rate}} = \frac{12.5\%}{5\%} = 2.5$$

According to Table 9.2, appraiser A is acceptable with percentage agreement, acceptable with the false alarm rate, and marginally acceptable with the leak rate. Depending on the level of risk acceptability, it may be necessary to reduce the leak rate.

Appraiser B is marginally acceptable with percentage agreement, unacceptable with the false alarm rate, and marginally acceptable with the leak rate. This appraiser should be retrained and their portion of the study reexecuted.

The leak rate is the most important of the three measurements as it records the number of defective products, which could be released to the customer (internal and external).

9.4 ATTRIBUTE R&R STUDY USING COHEN'S KAPPA STATISTIC

An *attribute R&R study using Cohen's kappa statistic* is used to access the inter-rater reliability for attribute or categorical data (rating). This method offers a statistically based rating rather than a traditional percentage agreement as used in other attribute gage R&R methods. This procedure utilizes a contingency table to access the inter-rater reliability. This method is limited to two appraisers; however, any number of categories can be used to assess the attribute measurement system. This method is best used to compare appraisers against known standards or reference parts.

Attribute R&R Study Using Cohen's Kappa Statistic Process

1. Determine the number of parts, trials, and appraisers necessary to conduct the study using a risk-based approach. To fully challenge the robustness and the ability of the measurement system, it is important to select some parts that are marginally considered good and marginally considered bad.

2. Establish acceptability criteria based on risk.

3. Allow sufficient time for environmental stabilization of the parts and gage if applicable.

4. Verify the calibration status of the gage if applicable.

5. Ensure that each appraiser is properly trained and has the necessary competence to perform the study.

6. Collect the data and fill in the attribute R&R study using Cohen's kappa statistic template as shown in Figure 9.8.

7. Complete a contingency table for each appraiser. The contingency table is completed by counting the number of appraiser passes as compared to the standard (PP), the number of appraiser fails with a pass standard (PF), the number of appraiser passes with a fail standard (FP), and the number of appraiser fails (FF) with a fail standard. Enter these counts into the

Part	Standard	Appraiser A		Appraiser B	
		Trial 1	Trial 2	Trial 1	Trial 2
1					
2					
3					
4					
5					
6					
7					
8					
9					
10					
11					
12					
13					
14					
15					
16					
17					
18					
19					
20					

Figure 9.8   Attribute R&R study using Cohen's kappa statistic template.

contingency table as shown in Figure 9.9 and total the rows and columns. Once these counts have been entered into the contingency table, calculate the expected values for each cell and enter the data into the table. Complete this step for each appraiser, with each appraiser having their own table.

8. Calculate Cohen's kappa statistic for each appraiser.

9. Analyze the results for each appraiser using the gage acceptability criteria provided in Table 9.3. Develop follow-up actions as necessary.

10. Document the reevaluation criteria and interval.

$$\text{Expected value} = \frac{\text{Row}_{\text{Total}} \times \text{Column}_{\text{Total}}}{n \times t}$$

$$\text{Kappa} = \frac{\text{PP}_{\text{Observed}} + \text{FF}_{\text{Observed}}}{n \times t} - \frac{\text{PP}_{\text{Expected}} + \text{FF}_{\text{Expected}}}{n \times t} \Big/ \left(1 - \frac{\text{PP}_{\text{Expected}} + \text{FF}_{\text{Expected}}}{n \times t}\right) \times 100$$

	Reference/standard		Total
	PP Observed / Expected	**PF** Observed / Expected	
Appraiser **FP** Observed / Expected		**FF** Observed / Expected	
Total			

FP = Number of fail/pass ratings PP = Number of pass/pass ratings
FF = Number of fail/fail ratings   PF = Number of pass/fail ratings

Figure 9.9   Cohen's kappa statistic contingency table.

Table 9.3   Gage acceptability criteria.

Agreement	Acceptance
> 75%	Acceptable
10% 75%	Marginally acceptable
< 40%	Unacceptable

where

n = Number of samples

t = Number of trials

Example: To verify the presence of a feature on a part, an attribute R&R study using Cohen's kappa statistic will be performed using 20 parts, two appraisers, and two trials. The completed assessment in shown in Figure 9.10.

The evaluation of the data in Figure 9.10 for the number of pass/pass ratings, number of pass/fail ratings, number of fail/pass ratings, and number of fail/fail ratings for each appraiser is displayed in the following contingency tables.

For appraiser A:

	Reference/standard		Total
Appraiser A **PP** 26 / 18.9		**PF** 2 / 9.1	28
FP 1 / 8.1		**FF** 11 / 3.9	12
Total	27	13	40

Part	Standard	Appraiser A		Appraiser B	
		Trial 1	Trial 2	Trial 1	Trial 2
1	P	(F)	P	P	P
2	P	P	P	(F)	P
3	F	F	F	F	F
4	P	P	P	P	P
5	F	(P)	F	F	F
6	P	P	P	P	P
7	P	P	P	P	P
8	P	P	(F)	P	P
9	P	P	P	P	P
10	P	P	P	(F)	(F)
11	F	F	F	F	F
12	P	P	P	(F)	P
13	P	P	P	(F)	P
14	P	P	P	P	P
15	P	P	P	P	(F)
16	P	P	P	P	P
17	F	F	F	F	F
18	F	F	F	(P)	F
19	P	P	P	P	P
20	F	F	F	F	F

Figure 9.10   Completed attribute R&R study using Cohen's kappa statistic template.

To calculate the expected values for appraiser A:

$$\text{Row 1 Column 1: Expected value} = \frac{\text{Row}_{\text{Total}} \times \text{Column}_{\text{Total}}}{n \times t} = \frac{28 \times 27}{20 \times 2} = 18.9$$

$$\text{Row 1 Column 2: Expected value} = \frac{\text{Row}_{\text{Total}} \times \text{Column}_{\text{Total}}}{n \times t} = \frac{28 \times 13}{20 \times 2} = 9.1$$

$$\text{Row 2 Column 1: Expected value} = \frac{\text{Row}_{\text{Total}} \times \text{Column}_{\text{Total}}}{n \times t} = \frac{12 \times 27}{20 \times 2} = 8.1$$

$$\text{Row 2 Column 2: Expected value} = \frac{\text{Row}_{\text{Total}} \times \text{Column}_{\text{Total}}}{n \times t} = \frac{12 \times 13}{20 \times 2} = 3.9$$

$$\text{Kappa} = \frac{\frac{\text{PP}_{\text{Observed}} + \text{FF}_{\text{Observed}}}{n \times t} - \frac{\text{PP}_{\text{Expected}} + \text{FF}_{\text{Expected}}}{n \times t}}{\left(1 - \frac{\text{PP}_{\text{Expected}} + \text{FF}_{\text{Expected}}}{n \times t}\right)} \times 100$$

$$\text{Kappa} = \frac{\frac{26+11}{20 \times 2} - \frac{18.9+3.9}{20 \times 2}}{\left(1 - \frac{18.9+3.9}{20 \times 2}\right)} \times 100 = 82.6\%$$

According to the gage acceptability criteria in Table 9.3, a kappa of 82.6% is considered to be acceptable.

For appraiser B:

		Reference/standard			Total
Appraiser B	PP	20 / 15.6	PF	6 / 10.4	26
	FP	4 / 8.4	FF	10 / 5.6	14
Total		24		16	40

To calculate the expected values for appraiser B:

$$\text{Row 1 Column 1: Expected value} = \frac{\text{Row}_{\text{Total}} \times \text{Column}_{\text{Total}}}{n \times t} = \frac{26 \times 24}{20 \times 2} = 15.6$$

$$\text{Row 1 Column 2: Expected value} = \frac{\text{Row}_{\text{Total}} \times \text{Column}_{\text{Total}}}{n \times t} = \frac{26 \times 16}{20 \times 2} = 10.4$$

$$\text{Row 2 Column 1: Expected value} = \frac{\text{Row}_{\text{Total}} \times \text{Column}_{\text{Total}}}{n \times t} = \frac{14 \times 24}{20 \times 2} = 8.4$$

$$\text{Row 2 Column 2: Expected value} = \frac{\text{Row}_{\text{Total}} \times \text{Column}_{\text{Total}}}{n \times t} = \frac{14 \times 16}{20 \times 2} = 5.6$$

$$\text{Kappa} = \frac{\frac{\text{PP}_{\text{Observed}} + \text{FF}_{\text{Observed}}}{n \times t} - \frac{\text{PP}_{\text{Expected}} + \text{FF}_{\text{Expected}}}{n \times t}}{\left(1 - \frac{\text{PP}_{\text{Expected}} + \text{FF}_{\text{Expected}}}{n \times t}\right)} \times 100$$

$$\text{Kappa} = \frac{\frac{20+10}{20 \times 2} - \frac{15.6+5.6}{20 \times 2}}{\left(1 - \frac{15.6+5.6}{20 \times 2}\right)} \times 100 = 46.8\%$$

According to the gage acceptability criteria in Table 9.3, a kappa of 46.8% is considered to be marginally acceptable.

9.5 ATTRIBUTE R&R STUDY USING FLEISS'S KAPPA STATISTIC

Unlike Cohen's kappa statistic, this method can use any number of appraisers and categories to assess the attribute measurement system. This statistic will be inflated when there are fewer categories. A good application of Fleiss's kappa statistic is when defects can be rated as minor, major, or critical (and, of course, no defect).

The Attribute R&R Study Using Fleiss's Kappa Statistic Process

1. Determine the number of parts, trials, and appraisers necessary to conduct the study using a risk-based approach. To fully challenge the robustness and the ability of the measurement system, it is important to select some parts that are marginally considered good and marginally considered bad.

2. Establish acceptability criteria based on risk.

3. Allow sufficient time for environmental stabilization of the parts and gage if applicable.

4. Verify the calibration status of the gage if applicable.

5. Ensure that each appraiser is properly trained and has the necessary competence to perform the study.

6. Collect the data and complete the attribute R&R study using Fleiss's kappa statistic template as shown in Figure 9.11.

Part	Defect			
	None	Minor	Major	Critical
1				
2				
3				
4				
5				
6				
7				
8				
9				
10				
Sum				

Figure 9.11   Attribute R&R study using Fleiss's kappa statistic template.

7. Calculate the column and row probabilities. Using the column and row probabilities, determine Fleiss's kappa statistic.

8. Analyze the results using Fleiss's kappa statistic interpretation provided in Table 9.4. Develop follow-up action as necessary.

9. Document the reevaluation criteria and interval.

$$p_{\text{None}} = \frac{\Sigma_{\text{None}}}{n \times r}$$

$$p_{\text{Minor}} = \frac{\Sigma_{\text{Minor}}}{n \times r}$$

$$p_{\text{Major}} = \frac{\Sigma_{\text{Major}}}{n \times r}$$

$$p_{\text{Critical}} = \frac{\Sigma_{\text{Critical}}}{n \times r}$$

$$p_{\text{Row 1}} = \frac{1}{r(r-1)} \left(\text{None}^2 + \text{Minor}^2 + \text{Major}^2 + \text{Critical}^2 - r \right)$$

$$p_{\text{Row 2}} = \frac{1}{r(r-1)} \left(\text{None}^2 + \text{Minor}^2 + \text{Major}^2 + \text{Critical}^2 - r \right)$$

$$p_{\text{Row 3}} = \frac{1}{r(r-1)} \left(\text{None}^2 + \text{Minor}^2 + \text{Major}^2 + \text{Critical}^2 - r \right)$$

$$p_{\text{Row 4}} = \frac{1}{r(r-1)} \left(\text{None}^2 + \text{Minor}^2 + \text{Major}^2 + \text{Critical}^2 - r \right)$$

$$p_{\text{Row 5}} = \frac{1}{r(r-1)} \left(\text{None}^2 + \text{Minor}^2 + \text{Major}^2 + \text{Critical}^2 - r \right)$$

Table 9.4 Interpreting Fleiss's kappa statistic.

K	Interpretation
< 0	Poor agreement
0.01–0.20	Slight agreement
0.21–0.40	Fair agreement
0.41–0.60	Moderate agreement
0.61–0.80	Substantial agreement
0.81–1.00	Almost perfect agreement

$$p_{\text{Row } 6} = \frac{1}{r(r-1)}\left(\text{None}^2 + \text{Minor}^2 + \text{Major}^2 + \text{Critical}^2 - r\right)$$

$$p_{\text{Row } 7} = \frac{1}{r(r-1)}\left(\text{None}^2 + \text{Minor}^2 + \text{Major}^2 + \text{Critical}^2 - r\right)$$

$$p_{\text{Row } 8} = \frac{1}{r(r-1)}\left(\text{None}^2 + \text{Minor}^2 + \text{Major}^2 + \text{Critical}^2 - r\right)$$

$$p_{\text{Row } 9} = \frac{1}{r(r-1)}\left(\text{None}^2 + \text{Minor}^2 + \text{Major}^2 + \text{Critical}^2 - r\right)$$

$$p_{\text{Row } 10} = \frac{1}{r(r-1)}\left(\text{None}^2 + \text{Minor}^2 + \text{Major}^2 + \text{Critical}^2 - r\right)$$

$$\overline{p}_{\text{Rows}} = \left[\Sigma\left(p_{\text{Row}}\right)\right]\frac{1}{n}$$

$$\overline{p}_{\text{Columns}} = p_{\text{None}}{}^2 + p_{\text{Minor}}{}^2 + p_{\text{Major}}{}^2 + p_{\text{Critical}}{}^2$$

$$\text{Kappa} = \frac{\overline{p}_{\text{Rows}} - \overline{p}_{\text{Columns}}}{1 - \overline{p}_{\text{Columns}}}$$

where

  n = Number of samples

  r = Number of appraisers

Example: Five appraisers are tasked with rating 10 samples to established criteria, determining whether there is a minor defect, major defect, critical defect, or no defect. The results of the evaluation are shown in Figure 9.12. Calculate Fleiss's kappa statistic and evaluate the result.

$$p_{\text{None}} = \frac{\Sigma_{\text{None}}}{n \times r} = \frac{10}{10 \times 5} = 0.20$$

$$p_{\text{Minor}} = \frac{\Sigma_{\text{Minor}}}{n \times r} = \frac{15}{10 \times 5} = 0.30$$

$$p_{\text{Major}} = \frac{\Sigma_{\text{Major}}}{n \times r} = \frac{15}{10 \times 5} = 0.30$$

$$p_{\text{Critical}} = \frac{\Sigma_{\text{Critical}}}{n \times r} = \frac{10}{10 \times 5} = 0.20$$

	Defect			
Part	None	Minor	Major	Critical
1	0	0	4	1
2	0	5	0	0
3	5	0	0	0
4	0	0	1	4
5	4	1	0	0
6	0	4	1	0
7	1	4	0	0
8	0	0	0	5
9	0	0	5	0
10	0	1	4	0
Sum	10	15	15	10

Figure 9.12　Completed attribute R&R study using Fleiss's kappa statistic.

$$p_{\text{Row 1}} = \frac{1}{r(r-1)}\left(\text{None}^2 + \text{Minor}^2 + \text{Major}^2 + \text{Critical}^2 - r\right)$$

$$= \frac{1}{5(5-1)}\left(0^2 + 0^2 + 4^2 + 1^2 - 5\right)$$

$$= 0.60$$

$$p_{\text{Row 2}} = \frac{1}{r(r-1)}\left(\text{None}^2 + \text{Minor}^2 + \text{Major}^2 + \text{Critical}^2 - r\right)$$

$$= \frac{1}{5(5-1)}\left(0^2 + 5^2 + 0^2 + 0^2 - 5\right)$$

$$= 1.00$$

$$p_{\text{Row 3}} = \frac{1}{r(r-1)}\left(\text{None}^2 + \text{Minor}^2 + \text{Major}^2 + \text{Critical}^2 - r\right)$$

$$= \frac{1}{5(5-1)}\left(5^2 + 0^2 + 0^2 + 0^2 - 5\right)$$

$$= 1.00$$

$$p_{\text{Row 4}} = \frac{1}{r(r-1)} \left(\text{None}^2 + \text{Minor}^2 + \text{Major}^2 + \text{Critical}^2 - r \right)$$

$$= \frac{1}{5(5-1)} \left(0^2 + 0^2 + 1^2 + 4^2 - 5 \right)$$

$$= 0.60$$

$$p_{\text{Row 5}} = \frac{1}{r(r-1)} \left(\text{None}^2 + \text{Minor}^2 + \text{Major}^2 + \text{Critical}^2 - r \right)$$

$$= \frac{1}{5(5-1)} \left(4^2 + 1^2 + 0^2 + 0^2 - 5 \right)$$

$$= 0.60$$

$$p_{\text{Row 6}} = \frac{1}{r(r-1)} \left(\text{None}^2 + \text{Minor}^2 + \text{Major}^2 + \text{Critical}^2 - r \right)$$

$$= \frac{1}{5(5-1)} \left(1^2 + 4^2 + 1^2 + 0^2 - 5 \right)$$

$$= 0.60$$

$$p_{\text{Row 7}} = \frac{1}{r(r-1)} \left(\text{None}^2 + \text{Minor}^2 + \text{Major}^2 + \text{Critical}^2 - r \right)$$

$$= \frac{1}{5(5-1)} \left(1^2 + 4^2 + 0^2 + 0^2 - 5 \right)$$

$$= 0.60$$

$$p_{\text{Row 8}} = \frac{1}{r(r-1)} \left(\text{None}^2 + \text{Minor}^2 + \text{Major}^2 + \text{Critical}^2 - r \right)$$

$$= \frac{1}{5(5-1)} \left(0^2 + 0^2 + 0^2 + 5^2 - 5 \right)$$

$$= 1.00$$

$$p_{\text{Row 9}} = \frac{1}{r(r-1)} \left(\text{None}^2 + \text{Minor}^2 + \text{Major}^2 + \text{Critical}^2 - r \right)$$

$$= \frac{1}{5(5-1)} \left(0^2 + 0^2 + 5^2 + 0^2 - 5 \right)$$

$$= 1.00$$

$$p_{\text{Row 10}} = \frac{1}{r(r-1)}\left(\text{None}^2 + \text{Minor}^2 + \text{Major}^2 + \text{Critical}^2 - r\right)$$

$$= \frac{1}{5(5-1)}\left(0^2 + 1^2 + 4^2 + 0^2 - 5\right)$$

$$= 0.60$$

$$\bar{p}_{\text{Rows}} = \left(\Sigma\left(p_{\text{Row}}\right)\right)\frac{1}{n}$$

$$= \left(0.60 + 1.00 + 1.00 + 0.60 + 0.60 + 0.60 + 0.60 + 1.00 + 1.00 + 0.60\right)\frac{1}{10}$$

$$= 0.76$$

$$\bar{p}_{\text{Columns}} = p_{\text{None}}{}^2 + p_{\text{Minor}}{}^2 + p_{\text{Major}}{}^2 + p_{\text{Critical}}{}^2$$

$$= 0.20^2 + 0.30^2 + 0.30^2 + 0.20^2$$

$$= 0.26$$

$$\text{Kappa} = \frac{\bar{p}_{\text{Rows}} - \bar{p}_{\text{Columns}}}{1 - \bar{p}_{\text{Columns}}} = \frac{0.76 - 0.26}{1 - 0.26} = 0.68$$

According to Table 9.4, Fleiss's kappa statistic of 0.68 is considered to have substantial agreement.

10

When the Results
Are Unacceptable

When the gage R&R results are unacceptable, by whatever criterion, it is necessary to know the source(s) of these results. Is the excessive measurement variation due primarily to repeatability (device)? Is it due primarily to reproducibility (appraisers)? Or is it the combination of both? The use of an effective problem-solving technique and tools such as brainstorming, plan–do–study–act (PDSA), fishbone analysis, root cause analysis (RCA), eight disciplines problem solving (8D), or other similar methodology will be beneficial in improving the measuring system. Knowing the answers to these questions allows you to evaluate which of several options to pursue:

1. The unacceptable results may be telling you what you need to know: either the device, the appraisers, or both are not doing the job that is required. Define and perform corrective action to assure that the device and operators are doing the best that is possible.

2. Further analysis and/or discussion with the device manufacturer may lead to the conclusion that the device is state-of-the-art and improvement is not possible. If so, document that conclusion and go to item 3.

3. If the dominant source of variation is *repeatability*, one way to improve precision is to average more than one test for the reported measurement. Averaging reduces the repeatability portion of the gage R&R by the square root of the number of measurements averaged. If such precision is truly needed and no other improvements are possible, the additional testing may be the only way to achieve that precision. This approach should not be used unless the testing procedures for production material are changed to apply this same technique to routine measurements. Is poor repeatability due to poor performance by all appraisers? Again, review training and procedures.

4. When appraisers (reproducibility) are the major source of variability, address training and standardization of procedures.

5. The specifications may be unrealistic. Does the customer really need them that tight?

6. Was there indication of, or reason to suspect, additional variation from incorrect calibration or variation within the sample? If so, it is now necessary to know if the unsatisfactory results are the result of those components. Design appropriate studies to isolate them.

7. If the process capability is adequate (the $C_p > 1.33$) despite the lack of precision, the inadequate gage R&R performance is not currently hindering the process and may not be an immediate priority. As process improvements are made, that situation will not last. Develop a timeline to start working toward measurement improvements.

   If the process capability is borderline ($1.0 \leq C_p \leq 1.33$), unacceptable gage R&R variation may make the difference in whether the observed process is reported as capable. If the process capability is clearly inadequate ($C_p < 1.0$), both measurement and process must be addressed. Measurement should be given priority in order to facilitate addressing the process.

8. A single index is not sufficient to clearly indicate the measurement and process status. It will always be helpful and desirable to use multiple indicators to fully comprehend the situation and priority. The two indices used for gage R&R assessments answer two different questions. Both questions may be of interest. The process capability measures also help in understanding the priority of measurement in the general improvement activity (see Chapter 8).

11

Special Considerations

Unfortunately, there are many measurement situations in industry in which standard procedures do not fit without modifications. This requires modifications to the procedures and/or calculations. Some examples are:

1. Significant variability within the sample being measured; for example, surface roundness

2. Instances in which there is no operator effect; for example, X-ray gage for thickness

3. Instruments that can not repeat measurements on the same part and therefore must be assessed off-line; for example, width gage on a high-speed mill

4. Destructive measurements that can not be repeated on the same item; for example, tensile tests

There is always more than one way to accomplish a gage R&R study. The most important requirement is thought and action in addressing measurement systems in a useful and meaningful manner. The fact that a typical R&R study is not possible in a given case should not prevent designing studies that can provide such data, at least in a static or calibration mode. This section contains descriptions of some procedures for performing gage R&R studies in unique cases. (Cases that clearly can be addressed with the standard procedures will be discussed only briefly.) The following procedures illustrate approaches applicable to many measurement devices, situations, and industries.

11.1 X-RAY GAGE

Measurement: Thickness. Thickness is measured by an X-ray unit as the material moves under the head. There is no operator influence on the X-ray reading, nor can the reading be repeated on exactly the same spot. The requirement becomes one of estimating the repeatability of the X-ray. It is not feasible to do this using production material. Instead, the test blocks used for calibration must be utilized and repeatability estimated in an off-line condition.

Randomize the order of test for the blocks, and report the results to the maximum available number of decimal places. Calculate repeatability by using the standard procedure. Note that there is no operator (treat such a situation as if there were a single operator) and that the number of test blocks determines the number of trials per block. The statistics for repeatability can be calculated, but there is no estimate for reproducibility. Since the reproducibility is zero, repeatability is the gage R&R.

Note 1: Determine the procedures used or recommended by the gage manufacturer. If they are compatible with or superior to the procedures proposed here, apply them.

Note 2: It is important that the repeatability is consistent across the range of thickness covered by the test blocks. If doubt arises over this, you may need to conduct a special study to see if it is necessary to divide the operating range into homogeneous categories. That is, you wish to assure that the average range for each test block is not significantly different from the others.

Note 3: Do not zero the system between test blocks unless that is also the procedure used in running production material.

Note 4: If nearly all the resulting ranges are zeros, there is inadequate measurement discrimination.

11.2 ELECTRONIC WIDTH GAGE

Measurement: Width. There is no operator effect on this measurement, nor can measurements be repeated on production material. Only an estimate of repeatability is appropriate in this case. The test pieces used to calibrate the device must be used to estimate repeatability.

Measure each of the test pieces in random order. That is, run the test pieces in random order and repeat the necessary number of times. If this is not practical, it may be necessary to run all the tests on a test piece before going to the next test piece. Report the results to as many decimal places as possible.

Calculate repeatability using the standard procedure. Since there is no operator, treat this case as if there were a single operator. The number of test pieces will determine the minimum number of trials. Only the repeatability can be estimated.

Note 1: Determine the procedures used or recommended by the gage manufacturer. If they are compatible or superior to the procedures proposed here, apply them.

Note 2: Examine manually generated width measurements with a standard gage R&R study of the device used.

Note 3: Do not zero the system between test blocks unless that is also the procedure used in running production material.

11.3 ELECTRONIC TEMPERATURE EQUIPMENT

Measurement: Temperature. Temperatures are measured by electronic equipment that provides results on material in high-speed operations. There is no opportunity for an operator to affect the measurements. It is also not possible to run meaningful repetitions of measurements with the equipment during actual operation. Since this equipment combines optical and electrical systems, use the calibration system to establish the repeatability of the equipment. There is no reproducibility in this case.

As part of the routine calibration of the system, repeatedly measure the test box (a calibrated source of electrical energy used to simulate the emissions of a hot product). This test unit should be measured at least 20 successive times. Plot the data as a moving range control chart. This permits a check on statistical control and allows estimation of the standard deviation by

$$\sigma_{EV} = \frac{\overline{mR}}{d_2} \quad \text{(See Appendix A for control chart constants)}$$

$$EV \text{ (repeatability)} = \frac{\sigma_{EV} \times 6}{TT \times 100} = GRR$$

where

TT = Total tolerance

d_2 = Number of measurements (see Appendix A, Control Chart Constants)

In this situation the GRR does not utilize reproducibility.

Note 1: If there is more than one test box or test setting, you must repeat the procedure.

Note 2: Solicit the manufacturer's advice to assure that the best and most reasonable procedure is used.

Note 3: The above calculation of σ can also be done directly on most pocket calculators.

However, the use of this approach does not determine whether the process is in statistical control.

11.4 CHEMICALS

Measurement: Chemical Analyses. Chemical analyses will fit the standard procedure for a gage R&R study. Take care to report results to as many decimal places as is possible, even if that is not the procedure of routine analyses. Use the standard procedure, with samples from a homogeneous range. Use routine samples unless there is evidence that an analysis is affected by variability within a sample. In that case, it will be necessary to use National Institute of Standards and Technology standards or any other source of extremely consistent material to permit a true gage R&R measurement.

Note 1: If you must carry out special studies or use special samples to avoid variability of material within the samples, this indicates the need for a separate study of this material variability. Such variation, a part of process capability, may be more important than the R&R study.

Note 2: Pay particular attention to the previous discussion of calibration procedures. It is essential that the calibration procedure of a chemical gage R&R be carefully defined and consistent for all operators. Similarly, the results should be consistently reported in the same fashion that production information is produced. In particular, if routine results provide the average of multiple analyses, then use that procedure here.

Note 3: If possible, perform the gage R&R on the same turn and not over a longer period.

Note 4: Be aware of the *lower limit of detection* (LLOD), *upper limit of detection* (ULOD), *lower limit of quantification* (LLOQ), and *upper limit of quantification* (ULOQ). These values can have a significant impact on the reliability of the measurement system and the R&R study.

11.5 SHEET FLATNESS

Measurement: Flatness. Flatness of steel blanks at an outside processor may be a key variable. Performance of a gage R&R study first requires that you adequately define the procedure for measuring flatness. Current procedures require placing a blank on a "flat" surface and measuring the distance from this surface to the bottom edge of the blank with a ruler. Such a measurement is probably made at the point of maximum apparent deviation; that is, an effort is made to estimate by eye the point most likely to exceed a specification. This procedure in a gage R&R would require applying the procedures of "attributes" (go/no-go) testing, requiring voluminous repetitions of measurements over a range of deviations from flatness that include the specification. While this can be done, it is much easier to make a quantitative measurement.

To approach this parameter as a "variables" measurement requires using an appropriate micrometer to measure the gap between the reference surface and the bottom of the blank. This micrometer should be capable of reading to at least three decimal places. The requirements then are:

1. Use a gage capable of measuring to at least three decimal places.

2. Assure that the reference surface is "flat."

3. Define where and how to make the measurement on a blank. That is, is the reported value to be the maximum of n tests on a blank? The average of n tests? The measurement of a single, randomly selected position? The eyeball estimate of the point of maximum deviation from planarity? How this measurement is defined is less important than the fact that it is indeed defined precisely and applied consistently.

4. Apply the standard procedure, with the following exceptions:

   a. Have each operator measure the same blank once while it is on the reference surface. Then have operators repeat the measurement without repositioning the blank. (The variability possibly induced by repositioning is equivalent to that of variability within a sample.)

b. Repeat this procedure for each of the randomly selected blanks.

11.6 PHYSICAL (DESTRUCTIVE) TESTS

Measurement: Physical Properties. Tests of physical properties (yield strength, tensile, modular R, elongation, hardness, LDH, and so on) are unique only in that most of these are destructive tests or can not be repeated in exactly the same position. In order to perform a gage R&R evaluation, you must obtain test pieces from adjacent areas of the sample to ensure homogeneity. Otherwise, the analysis is routine.

Obtain samples that cover the typical range of measured properties for a given category of product, that is, an appropriate grouping of grades or properties. From each sample, at least two test pieces per operator must be cut as close together as possible. In the case of tensile tests, for example, the test pieces should be adjacent pieces from the center of the coil sample. In the case of LDH tests, the test pieces should be adjacent pieces long enough to cut the five sub-pieces from adjacent areas.

Once the sample material has been selected and the test pieces prepared per the usual sample preparation procedures, randomly assign the test pieces to an operator. From this point, the analyses can utilize the standard form.

Note 1: The intent in preparing test pieces is to have the test pieces from a sample as identical as possible with respect to the properties being measured. This will require selecting the test pieces in a different manner from normal sample generation, where the intent is to represent the coil.

Note 2: Production samples should be used initially in these studies. If prior knowledge or an unsatisfactory repeatability estimate indicates the possibility of significant variability within the sample, standards must be used to separate the gage R&R variation from the material variation.

Note 3: Any dimensional measurements must be made to four decimal places.

Note 4: If all test pieces are not prepared by one operator at one time, be ready to explore sample preparation as a major source of variation. If sample prep is not directly involved in a gage R&R study, direct a separate study at this potential source of variation.

11.7 PROFILOMETERS

Measurement: Surface Texture. Surface texture is measured with a profilometer. These measurements are unique in that they are very susceptible to the variability within the test piece. Selection of samples, number of operators, and number of trials are subject to the usual logic for a standard study. However, you should apply the following additional procedures:

1. To minimize the effect of variability within the sample, mark the point of test. Each operator should run their tests at that same place.

2. A reported result should be the average of more than one test. Once the data are available, follow the standard analysis.

Note 1: Define the averaging technique by the proper standard. Use the current standard until data are available to determine the number of tests to average.

Note 2: It may be necessary to move the location of test enough after each test to avoid a "trench" effect. If so, material variability may become a factor.

11.8 MICROMETERS

Measurement: Dimensions. Many measurements are made with various types of micrometers. This is the classic application of the standard procedure. A random sample of operators and test material is used to carry out a typical R&R study on each device. Consistently report results to as many decimal places as possible. It is also important that the operators measure at the same place on each sample. Otherwise, the variability within the sample will intrude on the R&R study. Analysis uses the standard procedures.

Due to the large population of micrometers to be analyzed, a shortcut procedure was developed that may reduce the amount of testing. The key change in approach is to have each operator use a different micrometer for the gage R&R study. By doing so, the effect of reproducibility (the operator effect) is mixed (the statistical term is *confounded*) with that of the various gages (calibration effects). If the normal R&R estimates are acceptable, then several micrometers have been approved in one study; if the results are not acceptable, then an R&R study must be performed on each micrometer in order to isolate the gage R&R effects. The procedure is:

1. Maximize the number of operators in the study. It is recommended that you use four operators and 10 samples. This will allow four micrometers to be evaluated in one study.

2. Assign a different micrometer to each operator; each operator is to use this same micrometer for the entire study. Note that you will not be able to tell the difference between the effects of operator and micrometer.

3. Have each operator carry out at least two trials.

4. Analyze using the standard procedure. The only unique feature in the analysis is that reproducibility is actually a combination of the differences in operators, micrometers, and calibration. If the results are acceptable, there is no need to separate the mixed components in the reproducibility estimate; all the micrometers involved are acceptable. If the results are not acceptable, perform a separate gage R&R on each micrometer.

Note: This procedure is applicable to other device types where the number of devices is large.

11.9 SCALES AND BALANCES

A scale gage R&R is performed by making repeated measurements of the same item, whether that item is a test weight or a product. The gage R&R may be run over a short or long period of time, depending on the time available at the scale for making the measurements. There may not be an operator effect in most cases, although this should be considered carefully. (For instance, differences between operators in placement of the product on the scale may create a difference in measurements. If this is possible, consider an operator effect.)

Case A: Short-Term Studies

1. Calibrate the scale, or assure that it is within the required calibration period.

2. Weigh the test weight or the product. If the scale is routinely zeroed before each measurement, do this. If not, don't.

3. Remove the weight.

4. Repeat steps 2 and 3 until you have made 20 measurements.

5. Calculate the standard deviation of these measurements as the σ of repeatability.

Method 1. Plot a moving range control chart from the time-ordered data. Verify statistical control and calculate the standard deviation as

$$\sigma_{EV} = \frac{\overline{mR}}{d_2} \text{ (See Appendix A for control chart constants)}$$

$$EV \text{ (repeatability)} = \frac{\sigma_{EV} \times 6}{TT \times 100} = GRR$$

where

TT = Total tolerance

d_2 = Number of measurements (see Appendix A, Control Chart Constants)

In this situation the GRR does not utilize reproducibility.

Method 2. Calculate the sample standard deviation (σ).

Case B: Long-Term Studies

1. Calibrate the scale.

2. Weigh the test weight or the product. If the scale is routinely zeroed before each measurement, do so here. If not, don't.

3. Remove the weight.

4. Repeat steps 2 and 3 twice more.

5. At the next regular scale calibration, repeat steps 1 through 4.

6. Repeat this procedure (steps 1 through 5) until at least eight sets of three measurements are accumulated.

7. Analyze, except treat each set of three measurements as a sample. That is, the eight time periods act as samples, while the three measurements at each time period are the trials.

Note 1: The procedures described above assume that there is no operator effect. If there is concern or question about this point, then repeat each of the above procedures for each operator used in the study. The standard procedure is directly applicable.

Note 2: If, as part of calibration control, you maintain a control chart for ranges on repeated measurements of a test weight, you can use that control chart in place of these procedures. Note that such a control chart is nothing more than a range chart of the data in procedure 2. The $\bar{R}$ can be used to estimate repeatability by using

$$\sigma_{EV} = \frac{\bar{R}}{d_2} \text{ (See Appendix A for control chart constants)}$$

where

d_2 = Number of measurements (see Appendix A, Control Chart Constants)

Note 3: If the calibration procedure is not currently control-charted, it would be very useful to establish an $\bar{X}$ and R chart on the data generated in case B. The R chart, as note 2 indicates, covers the gage R&R. The $\bar{X}$ chart would be useful in assessing the effectiveness of the calibration procedure.

11.10 BORE GAGE

Measurement: Tubing Inside Diameter. A bore gage measures the inside diameter of steel tubing. Insert the gage into the tube resting on the three positioning prongs. The gage must be held parallel to the tube and held steady. As you rotate the gage in the tube, the "measurement" prong follows the contour of the inside diameter of the tube, with the dial indicating the diameter. Studies may analyze the diameter, the *ovality* (maximum diameter minus minimum diameter), or the maximum and minimum diameters separately.

To perform a gage R&R study:

1. Calibrate or verify the bore gage.

2. Select operators and samples for the study.

3. Instruct operators to measure at the same distance from the end of the tube.

4. Each operator measures the samples (trial 1).

5. Repeat the trials the necessary number of times.

6. Use the standard procedure.

Note 1: Consistent lack of planarity by an operator in holding the gage will enlarge the reported reproducibility; inconsistency in planarity will enlarge the reported repeatability.

Note 2: Variation in the depth within the tube at which the measurements are made may introduce variation from within the sample. Consistent differences between appraisers in location may enlarge the reported reproducibility; inconsistent differences may enlarge reported repeatability.

11.11 NUCLEAR MOISTURE GAGE

Measurement: Moisture. A nuclear moisture gage is an electronic device mounted at a weigh hopper or material transfer point that measures the hydrogen atoms in the material in the immediate vicinity of the device head. This reading is translated into an estimate of moisture via a calibration curve that is validated periodically. As soon as the gage has completed the measurement, the estimated moisture is printed and the material is transferred. Due to the brief time available and the necessity to avoid delaying a time-sensitive operation, the problem is how to carry out a meaningful gage R&R study.

In this situation, there is no operator effect. Since we are dealing only with repeatability, recall that repeatability, as the name implies, stems from repeated measurements of the same material by a measurement device. In this situation, the device can not return at a later time to repeat this measurement, as would be the procedure in a standard R&R study; the only way to repeat the measurement is to do it immediately. Since such operations are time-sensitive already, it would be difficult for operations to wait for more than two successive readings; in fact, such repeated measurements may need to be spread over several days to avoid affecting the operating rate. It may be desirable anyway to carry out the study over a range of moisture conditions.

Therefore, use the following procedure:

1. Since there is no operator effect, treat this case as if there were a single operator.

2. Make the usual measurement on a weigh hopper, then immediately repeat the measurement. You must do this when the material is not moving. This allows the device to sense the moisture in exactly the same material as the first reading.

3. Repeat this procedure over several days to obtain the specified number of pairs. These could be done, for example, at the rate of two pairs per day until the required number is satisfied.

4. Analyze as usual, using the standard procedure.

Note: If the moisture gage requires recalibration during this program, you must repeat the study after the recalibration.

12

Conclusion

The continuous improvement philosophy is essential in the realm of measurement. It is a realm where no procedure holds universally. Each device or situation must be thoughtfully considered and appropriate procedures tailored to fit the conditions of the complete gage R&R life cycle.

Gage R&R studies provide an opportunity to improve your process and reduce variation, thereby reducing costs. Establishment of an index or criterion does not mean that any correctable measurement problem should be tolerated. Even if not a priority, the continuous improvement philosophy requires that corrective action be defined and a timetable assigned to accomplish it. The intent with gage R&R studies is that they are to be part of an ongoing, comprehensive system, not just performed once and forgotten.

This book has covered the basic concepts for gage R&R—repeatability and reproducibility. In conclusion, refer again to Figure 1.1 and remember that other components of measurement variation are assumed to be negligible. By ignoring any significant contributions from other components of measurement, we have included them with the estimate of process variation. Once a gage R&R program is under way, it is important to evaluate calibration, stability, and linearity. An effective gage R&R program should tie into a comprehensive calibration program.

It should be obvious from the examples provided that the required calculations can be completed using spreadsheet applications or dedicated statistical programs. However, all of the examples were worked using a simple scientific calculator. Whichever way is used, make sure you understand the underlying assumptions and calculations that were used to generate the answer.

If the examples throughout the book are worked using a spreadsheet or a commercially available software package instead of a simple scientific calculator, the results can and will vary. The differences are attributable to rounding errors. Although there are differences, essentially the same results and conclusions will be obtained.

One last consideration: make sure that the measurement system and criteria in use match at the customer and supplier. Ensure that the environmental conditions (temperature, humidity, light, and so on) are the same. It is also very important to make sure that the gage hardware (and software if applicable) is at the same revision level. These simple considerations can save hours of material review board (MRB) disposition meetings!

Finally, go perform some gage R&R studies. After performing some studies, it will be obvious that establishing and maintaining a measurement systems analysis program is neither as difficult nor as massive as one might assume. Good luck!

Appendix A
Control Chart Constants

(n)	A	A₂	D₁	D₂	D₃	D₄	A₃	B₃	B₄	d₂	d₃	c₄
2	2.121	1.880	0.000	3.686	0.000	3.267	2.659	0.000	3.267	1.128	0.853	0.798
3	1.732	1.023	0.000	4.358	0.000	2.574	1.954	0.000	2.568	1.693	0.888	0.886
4	1.500	0.729	0.000	4.698	0.000	2.282	1.628	0.000	2.266	2.059	0.880	0.921
5	1.342	0.577	0.000	4.918	0.000	2.114	1.427	0.000	2.089	2.326	0.864	0.940
6	1.225	0.483	0.000	5.078	0.000	2.004	1.287	0.030	1.970	2.534	0.848	0.952
7	1.134	0.419	0.204	5.204	0.076	1.924	1.182	0.118	1.882	2.704	0.833	0.959
8	1.061	0.373	0.388	5.306	0.136	1.864	1.099	0.185	1.815	2.847	0.820	0.965
9	1.000	0.337	0.547	5.393	0.184	1.816	1.032	0.239	1.761	2.970	0.808	0.969
10	0.949	0.308	0.687	5.469	0.223	1.777	0.975	0.284	1.716	3.078	0.797	0.973
11	0.905	0.285	0.811	5.535	0.256	1.744	0.927	0.321	1.679	3.173	0.787	0.975
12	0.866	0.266	0.922	5.594	0.283	1.717	0.886	0.354	1.646	3.258	0.778	0.978
13	0.832	0.249	1.025	5.647	0.307	1.693	0.850	0.382	1.618	3.336	0.770	0.979
14	0.802	0.235	1.118	5.696	0.328	1.672	0.817	0.406	1.594	3.407	0.763	0.981
15	0.775	0.223	1.203	5.741	0.347	1.653	0.789	0.428	1.572	3.472	0.756	0.982
16	0.750	0.212	1.282	5.782	0.363	1.637	0.763	0.448	1.552	3.532	0.750	0.984
17	0.728	0.203	1.356	5.820	0.378	1.622	0.739	0.466	1.534	3.588	0.744	0.985
18	0.707	0.194	1.424	5.856	0.391	1.608	0.718	0.482	1.518	3.640	0.739	0.985
19	0.688	0.187	1.487	5.891	0.403	1.597	0.698	0.497	1.503	3.689	0.733	0.986
20	0.671	0.180	1.549	5.921	0.415	1.585	0.680	0.510	1.490	3.735	0.729	0.987
21	0.655	0.173	1.605	5.951	0.425	1.575	0.663	0.523	1.477	3.778	0.724	0.988
22	0.640	0.167	1.659	5.979	0.434	1.566	0.647	0.534	1.466	3.819	0.720	0.988
23	0.626	0.162	1.710	6.006	0.443	1.557	0.633	0.545	1.455	3.858	0.716	0.989
24	0.612	0.157	1.759	6.031	0.451	1.548	0.619	0.555	1.445	3.895	0.712	0.989
25	0.600	0.153	1.806	6.056	0.459	1.541	0.606	0.565	1.435	3.931	0.708	0.990

Appendix B
C_2 Correction Factors

z	W													
	2	3	4	5	6	7	8	9	10	11	12	13	14	15
1	1.414	1.912	2.239	2.481	2.673	2.83	2.963	3.078	3.179	3.269	3.35	3.424	3.491	3.553
2	1.279	1.805	2.151	2.405	2.604	2.768	2.906	3.025	3.129	3.221	3.305	3.38	3.449	3.513
3	1.231	1.769	2.12	2.379	2.581	2.747	2.886	3.006	3.112	3.205	3.289	3.366	3.435	3.499
4	1.206	1.75	2.105	2.366	2.57	2.736	2.877	2.997	3.103	3.197	3.282	3.358	3.428	3.492
5	1.191	1.739	2.096	2.358	2.563	2.73	2.871	2.992	3.098	3.192	3.277	3.354	3.424	3.488
6	1.181	1.731	2.09	2.353	2.558	2.726	2.867	2.988	3.095	3.189	3.274	3.351	3.421	3.486
7	1.173	1.726	2.085	2.349	2.555	2.723	2.864	2.986	3.092	3.187	3.272	3.349	3.419	3.484
8	1.168	1.721	2.082	2.346	2.552	2.72	2.862	2.984	3.09	3.185	3.27	3.347	3.417	3.482
9	1.164	1.718	2.08	2.344	2.55	2.719	2.86	2.982	3.089	3.184	3.269	3.346	3.416	3.481
10	1.16	1.716	2.077	2.342	2.549	2.717	2.859	2.981	3.088	3.183	3.268	3.345	3.415	3.48
11	1.157	1.714	2.076	2.34	2.547	2.716	2.858	2.98	3.087	3.182	3.267	3.344	3.415	3.479
12	1.155	1.712	2.074	2.3439	2.546	2.715	2.857	2.979	3.086	3.181	3.266	3.343	3.414	3.479
13	1.153	1.71	2.073	2.338	2.545	2.714	2.856	2.978	3.085	3.18	3.266	3.343	3.413	3.478
14	1.151	1.709	2.072	2.337	2.545	2.714	2.856	2.978	3.085	3.18	3.265	3.342	3.413	3.478
15	1.15	1.708	2.071	2.337	2.544	2.713	2.855	2.977	3.084	3.179	3.265	3.342	3.412	3.477
>15	1.128	1.693	2.059	2.326	2.534	2.704	2.847	2.97	3.078	3.173	3.259	3.336	3.407	3.472

Appendix C

Selected Percentages of the *F*-Distribution

	Percentages of the *F*-Distribution $\alpha = 0.01$											
	Degrees of freedom for numerator $\nu 1$											
$\nu 2$	1	2	5	6	7	8	9	10	12	14	16	18
20	8.10	5.85	4.10	3.87	3.70	3.56	3.46	3.37	3.23	3.13	3.05	2.99
24	7.82	5.61	3.90	3.67	3.50	3.36	3.26	3.17	3.03	2.93	2.85	2.79
25	7.77	5.57	3.85	3.63	3.46	3.32	3.22	3.13	2.99	2.89	2.81	2.75
28	7.64	5.45	3.75	3.53	3.36	3.23	3.12	3.03	2.90	2.79	2.72	2.65
30	7.56	5.39	3.70	3.47	3.30	3.17	3.07	2.98	2.84	2.74	2.66	2.60
32	7.50	5.34	3.65	3.43	3.26	3.13	3.02	2.93	2.80	2.70	2.62	2.55
35	7.42	5.27	3.59	3.37	3.20	3.07	2.96	2.88	2.74	2.64	2.56	2.50
36	7.40	5.25	3.57	3.35	3.18	3.05	2.95	2.86	2.72	2.62	2.54	2.48
40	7.31	5.18	3.51	3.29	3.12	2.99	2.89	2.80	2.66	2.56	2.48	2.42
42	7.28	5.15	3.49	3.27	3.10	2.97	2.86	2.78	2.64	2.54	2.46	2.40
45	7.23	5.11	3.45	3.23	3.07	2.94	2.83	2.74	2.61	2.51	2.43	2.36
48	7.19	5.08	3.43	3.20	3.04	2.91	2.80	2.71	2.58	2.48	2.40	2.33
50	7.17	5.06	3.41	3.19	3.02	2.89	2.78	2.70	2.56	2.46	2.38	2.32
54	7.13	5.02	3.38	3.16	2.99	2.86	2.76	2.67	2.53	2.43	2.35	2.29
60	7.08	4.98	3.34	3.12	2.95	2.82	2.72	2.63	2.50	2.39	2.31	2.25
65	7.04	4.95	3.31	3.09	2.93	2.80	2.69	2.61	2.47	2.37	2.29	2.23
66	7.04	4.94	3.31	3.09	2.92	2.79	2.69	2.60	2.47	2.36	2.28	2.22
67	7.03	4.94	3.30	3.08	2.92	2.79	2.68	2.60	2.46	2.36	2.28	2.22
68	7.02	4.93	3.30	3.08	2.91	2.78	2.68	2.59	2.46	2.36	2.28	2.21
69	7.02	4.93	3.29	3.08	2.91	2.78	2.68	2.59	2.45	2.35	2.27	2.21
70	7.01	4.92	3.29	3.07	2.91	2.78	2.67	2.59	2.45	2.35	2.27	2.20
72	7.00	4.91	3.28	3.06	2.90	2.77	2.66	2.58	2.44	2.34	2.26	2.20
74	6.99	4.90	3.28	3.06	2.89	2.76	2.66	2.57	2.43	2.33	2.25	2.19
76	6.98	4.90	3.27	3.05	2.88	2.75	2.65	2.56	2.43	2.33	2.25	2.18
78	6.97	4.89	3.26	3.04	2.88	2.75	2.64	2.56	2.42	2.32	2.24	2.17
79	6.97	4.88	3.26	3.04	2.87	2.75	2.64	2.55	2.42	2.32	2.24	2.17
80	6.96	4.88	3.26	3.04	2.87	2.74	2.64	2.55	2.42	2.31	2.23	2.17

	Percentages of the *F*-Distribution α = 0.05											
	Degrees of freedom for numerator ν1											
ν2	1	2	5	6	7	8	9	10	12	14	16	18
20	4.35	3.49	2.71	2.60	2.51	2.45	2.39	2.35	2.28	2.22	2.18	2.15
24	4.26	3.40	2.62	2.51	2.42	2.36	2.30	2.25	2.18	2.13	2.09	2.05
25	4.24	3.39	2.60	2.49	2.40	2.34	2.28	2.24	2.16	2.11	2.07	2.04
28	4.20	3.34	2.56	2.45	2.36	2.29	2.24	2.19	2.12	2.06	2.02	1.99
30	4.17	3.32	2.53	2.42	2.33	2.27	2.21	2.16	2.09	2.04	1.99	1.96
32	4.15	3.29	2.51	2.40	2.31	2.24	2.19	2.14	2.07	2.01	1.97	1.94
35	4.12	3.27	2.49	2.37	2.29	2.22	2.16	2.11	2.04	1.99	1.94	1.91
36	4.11	3.26	2.48	2.36	2.28	2.21	2.15	2.11	2.03	1.98	1.93	1.90
40	4.08	3.23	2.45	2.34	2.25	2.18	2.12	2.08	2.00	1.95	1.90	1.87
42	4.07	3.22	2.44	2.32	2.24	2.17	2.11	2.06	1.99	1.94	1.89	1.86
45	4.06	3.20	2.42	2.31	2.22	2.15	2.10	2.05	1.97	1.92	1.87	1.84
48	4.04	3.19	2.41	2.29	2.21	2.14	2.08	2.03	1.96	1.90	1.86	1.82
50	4.03	3.18	2.40	2.29	2.20	2.13	2.07	2.03	1.95	1.89	1.85	1.81
54	4.02	3.17	2.39	2.27	2.18	2.12	2.06	2.01	1.94	1.88	1.83	1.80
60	4.00	3.15	2.37	2.25	2.17	2.10	2.04	1.99	1.92	1.86	1.82	1.78
65	3.99	3.14	2.36	2.24	2.15	2.08	2.03	1.98	1.90	1.85	1.80	1.76
66	3.99	3.14	2.35	2.24	2.15	2.08	2.03	1.98	1.90	1.84	1.80	1.76
67	3.98	3.13	2.35	2.24	2.15	2.08	2.02	1.98	1.90	1.84	1.80	1.76
68	3.98	3.13	2.35	2.24	2.15	2.08	2.02	1.97	1.90	1.84	1.79	1.76
69	3.98	3.13	2.35	2.23	2.15	2.08	2.02	1.97	1.90	1.84	1.79	1.76
70	3.98	3.13	2.35	2.23	2.14	2.07	2.02	1.97	1.89	1.84	1.79	1.75
72	3.97	3.12	2.34	2.23	2.14	2.07	2.01	1.96	1.89	1.83	1.79	1.75
74	3.97	3.12	2.34	2.22	2.14	2.07	2.01	1.96	1.89	1.83	1.78	1.74
76	3.97	3.12	2.33	2.22	2.13	2.06	2.01	1.96	1.88	1.82	1.78	1.74
78	3.96	3.11	2.33	2.22	2.13	2.06	2.00	1.95	1.88	1.82	1.77	1.74
79	3.96	3.11	2.33	2.22	2.13	2.06	2.00	1.95	1.88	1.82	1.77	1.74
80	3.96	3.11	2.33	2.21	2.13	2.06	2.00	1.95	1.88	1.82	1.77	1.73

Percentages of the *F*-Distribution α = 0.10

v2	Degrees of freedom for numerator v1											
	1	2	5	6	7	8	9	10	12	14	16	18
20	2.97	2.59	2.16	2.09	2.04	2.00	1.96	1.94	1.89	1.86	1.83	1.81
24	2.93	2.54	2.10	2.04	1.98	1.94	1.91	1.88	1.83	1.80	1.77	1.75
25	2.92	2.53	2.09	2.02	1.97	1.93	1.89	1.87	1.82	1.79	1.76	1.74
28	2.89	2.50	2.06	2.00	1.94	1.90	1.87	1.84	1.79	1.75	1.73	1.70
30	2.88	2.49	2.05	1.98	1.93	1.88	1.85	1.82	1.77	1.74	1.71	1.69
32	2.87	2.48	2.04	1.97	1.91	1.87	1.83	1.81	1.76	1.72	1.69	1.67
35	2.85	2.46	2.02	1.95	1.90	1.85	1.82	1.79	1.74	1.70	1.67	1.65
36	2.85	2.46	2.01	1.94	1.89	1.85	1.81	1.78	1.73	1.70	1.67	1.65
40	2.84	2.44	2.00	1.93	1.87	1.83	1.79	1.76	1.71	1.68	1.65	1.62
42	2.83	2.43	1.99	1.92	1.86	1.82	1.78	1.75	1.71	1.67	1.64	1.62
45	2.82	2.42	1.98	1.91	1.85	1.81	1.77	1.74	1.70	1.66	1.63	1.60
48	2.81	2.42	1.97	1.90	1.85	1.80	1.77	1.73	1.69	1.65	1.62	1.59
50	2.81	2.41	1.97	1.90	1.84	1.80	1.76	1.73	1.68	1.64	1.61	1.59
54	2.80	2.40	1.96	1.89	1.83	1.79	1.75	1.72	1.67	1.63	1.60	1.58
60	2.79	2.39	1.95	1.87	1.82	1.77	1.74	1.71	1.66	1.62	1.59	1.56
65	2.78	2.39	1.94	1.87	1.81	1.77	1.73	1.70	1.65	1.61	1.58	1.55
66	2.78	2.38	1.94	1.87	1.81	1.77	1.73	1.70	1.65	1.61	1.58	1.55
67	2.78	2.38	1.94	1.86	1.81	1.76	1.73	1.70	1.65	1.61	1.58	1.55
68	2.78	2.38	1.93	1.86	1.81	1.76	1.73	1.69	1.64	1.61	1.58	1.55
69	2.78	2.38	1.93	1.86	1.81	1.76	1.72	1.69	1.64	1.60	1.57	1.55
70	2.78	2.38	1.93	1.86	1.80	1.76	1.72	1.69	1.64	1.60	1.57	1.55
72	2.78	2.38	1.93	1.86	1.80	1.76	1.72	1.69	1.64	1.60	1.57	1.54
74	2.77	2.38	1.93	1.86	1.80	1.75	1.72	1.69	1.64	1.60	1.57	1.54
76	2.77	2.37	1.92	1.85	1.80	1.75	1.72	1.68	1.63	1.59	1.56	1.54
78	2.77	2.37	1.92	1.85	1.80	1.75	1.71	1.68	1.63	1.59	1.56	1.54
79	2.77	2.37	1.92	1.85	1.79	1.75	1.71	1.68	1.63	1.59	1.56	1.54
80	2.77	2.37	1.92	1.85	1.79	1.75	1.71	1.68	1.63	1.59	1.56	1.53

Appendix D
Critical Values of the Correlation Coefficient

df (n − 2)	α values				df (n − 2)	α values			
	0.1	0.05	0.02	0.01		0.1	0.05	0.02	0.01
1	.988	.997	1.000	1.000	21	.352	.413	.482	.526
2	.900	.950	.980	.990	22	.344	.404	.472	.515
3	.805	.878	.934	.959	23	.337	.396	.462	.505
4	.729	.811	.882	.917	24	.330	.388	.453	.496
5	.669	.754	.833	.874	25	.323	.381	.445	.487
6	.622	.707	.789	.834	26	.317	.374	.437	.479
7	.582	.666	.750	.798	27	.311	.367	.430	.471
8	.549	.632	.716	.765	28	.306	.361	.423	.463
9	.521	.602	.685	.735	29	.301	.355	.416	.456
10	.497	.576	.658	.708	30	.296	.349	.409	.449
11	.476	.553	.634	.684	35	.275	.325	.381	.418
12	.458	.532	.612	.661	40	.257	.304	.358	.393
13	.441	.514	.592	.641	45	.243	.288	.338	.372
14	.426	.497	.574	.623	50	.231	.273	.322	.354
15	.412	.482	.558	.606	60	.211	.250	.295	.325
16	.400	.468	.542	.590	70	.195	.232	.274	.303
17	.389	.456	.528	.575	80	.183	.217	.256	.283
18	.378	.444	.516	.561	90	.173	.205	.242	.267
19	.369	.433	.503	.549	100	.164	.195	.230	.254
20	.360	.423	.492	.537					

Appendix E
Student's *t*-Distribution

df	*p* α	0.9 0.1	0.95 0.05	0.975 0.025	0.9875 0.0125	0.995 0.005	0.9975 0.0025	0.999 0.001	0.9995 0.0005
1		3.078	6.314	12.706	25.452	63.657	127.321	318.309	636.619
2		1.886	2.920	4.303	6.205	9.925	14.089	22.327	31.599
3		1.638	2.353	3.182	4.177	5.841	7.453	10.215	12.924
4		1.533	2.132	2.776	3.495	4.604	5.598	7.173	8.610
5		1.476	2.015	2.571	3.163	4.032	4.773	5.893	6.869
6		1.440	1.943	2.447	2.969	3.707	4.317	5.208	5.959
7		1.415	1.895	2.365	2.841	3.499	4.029	4.705	5.400
8		1.397	1.860	2.306	2.752	3.355	3.833	4.501	5.041
9		1.383	1.833	2.262	2.685	3.250	3.690	4.297	4.781
10		1.372	1.812	2.228	2.634	3.169	3.581	4.144	4.587
11		1.363	1.796	2.201	2.593	3.106	3.497	4.025	4.437
12		1.356	1.782	2.179	2.560	3.055	3.428	3.930	4.318
13		1.350	1.771	2.160	2.533	3.012	3.372	3.852	4.221
14		1.345	1.761	2.145	2.510	2.977	3.326	3.787	4.140
15		1.341	1.753	2.131	2.490	2.947	3.286	3.733	4.073
16		1.337	1.746	2.120	2.473	2.921	3.252	3.686	4.015
17		1.333	1.740	2.110	2.458	2.898	3.222	3.646	3.965
18		1.330	1.734	2.101	2.445	2.878	3.197	3.610	3.922
19		1.328	1.729	2.093	2.433	2.861	3.174	3.579	3.883
20		1.325	1.725	2.086	2.423	2.845	3.153	3.552	3.850
21		1.323	1.721	2.080	2.414	2.831	3.135	3.527	3.819

Continued

Continued

df	p α	0.9 0.1	0.95 0.05	0.975 0.025	0.9875 0.0125	0.995 0.005	0.9975 0.0025	0.999 0.001	0.9995 0.0005
22		1.321	1.717	2.074	2.405	2.819	3.119	3.505	3.792
23		1.319	1.714	2.069	2.398	2.807	3.104	3.485	3.768
24		1.318	1.711	2.064	2.391	2.797	3.090	3.467	3.745
25		1.316	1.708	2.060	2.385	2.787	3.078	3.450	3.725
26		1.315	1.706	2.056	2.379	2.779	3.067	3.435	3.707
27		1.314	1.703	2.052	2.373	2.771	3.057	3.421	3.690
28		1.313	1.701	2.048	2.368	2.763	3.047	3.408	3.674
29		1.311	1.699	2.045	2.364	2.756	3.038	3.396	3.659
30		1.310	1.697	2.042	2.360	2.750	3.030	3.385	3.646
60		1.296	1.671	2.000	2.299	2.660	2.915	3.232	3.460
90		1.291	1.662	1.987	2.280	2.632	2.878	3.183	3.402
120		1.289	1.658	1.980	2.270	2.617	2.860	3.160	3.373
∞		1.282	1.645	1.960	2.242	2.576	2.807	3.090	3.291

Appendix F
Guard Banding Table

GRR %	Threshold percentage					
	70	80	90	95	99	100
1	0.004	0.004	0.005	0.005	0.005	0.005
2	0.009	0.009	0.009	0.010	0.010	0.010
3	0.013	0.013	0.014	0.014	0.015	0.015
4	0.017	0.018	0.018	0.019	0.020	0.020
5	0.021	0.022	0.023	0.024	0.025	0.025
6	0.026	0.027	0.027	0.029	0.030	0.030
7	0.030	0.031	0.032	0.033	0.035	0.035
8	0.034	0.036	0.036	0.038	0.040	0.040
9	0.038	0.040	0.041	0.043	0.045	0.045
10	0.043	0.045	0.045	0.048	0.050	0.050
11	0.047	0.049	0.050	0.052	0.054	0.055
12	0.051	0.053	0.054	0.057	0.059	0.060
13	0.056	0.058	0.059	0.062	0.064	0.065
14	0.060	0.062	0.063	0.067	0.069	0.070
15	0.064	0.067	0.068	0.071	0.074	0.075
16	0.068	0.071	0.072	0.076	0.079	0.080
17	0.073	0.076	0.077	0.081	0.084	0.085
18	0.077	0.080	0.081	0.086	0.089	0.090
19	0.081	0.085	0.086	0.090	0.094	0.095
20	0.086	0.089	0.090	0.095	0.099	0.100
21	0.090	0.094	0.095	0.100	0.104	0.105
22	0.094	0.098	0.099	0.105	0.109	0.110
23	0.098	0.102	0.104	0.109	0.114	0.115
24	0.103	0.107	0.108	0.114	0.119	0.120
25	0.107	0.111	0.113	0.119	0.124	0.125

Note: Always round the GRR% up to the next whole percentage.   *Continued*

Continued

GRR	Threshold percentage					
%	70	80	90	95	99	100
26	0.111	0.116	0.117	0.124	0.129	0.130
27	0.115	0.120	0.122	0.128	0.134	0.135
28	0.120	0.125	0.126	0.133	0.139	0.140
29	0.124	0.129	0.131	0.138	0.144	0.145
30	0.128	0.134	0.135	0.143	0.149	0.150
31	0.133	0.138	0.140	0.147	0.153	0.155
32	0.137	0.143	0.144	0.152	0.158	0.160
33	0.141	0.147	0.149	0.157	0.163	0.165
34	0.145	0.151	0.153	0.162	0.168	0.170
35	0.150	0.156	0.158	0.166	0.173	0.175
36	0.154	0.160	0.162	0.171	0.178	0.180
37	0.158	0.165	0.167	0.176	0.183	0.185
38	0.162	0.169	0.171	0.181	0.188	0.190
39	0.167	0.174	0.176	0.185	0.193	0.195
40	0.171	0.178	0.180	0.190	0.198	0.200
41	0.175	0.183	0.185	0.195	0.203	0.205
42	0.180	0.187	0.189	0.200	0.208	0.210
43	0.184	0.192	0.194	0.204	0.213	0.215
44	0.188	0.196	0.198	0.209	0.218	0.220
45	0.192	0.200	0.203	0.214	0.223	0.225
46	0.197	0.205	0.207	0.219	0.228	0.230
47	0.201	0.209	0.212	0.223	0.233	0.235
48	0.205	0.214	0.216	0.228	0.238	0.240
49	0.209	0.218	0.221	0.233	0.243	0.245
50	0.214	0.223	0.225	0.238	0.248	0.250

Note: Always round the GRR% up to the next whole percentage.

Appendix G
Gage R&R Study Procedure

SOP 111 Rev A Measurement System Analysis (MSA)/Test Method Validations (TMV)

1.0 PURPOSE

The purpose of this procedure is to provide guidelines for conducting attribute and variable measurement systems analysis (MSA)/test method validations (TMV).

MSA/TMV validations will be performed to assess the suitability of measurement systems to ensure their adequacy for making quality decisions.

2.0 SCOPE

This procedure applies to the validations performed on gages used by Acme Medical Device LLC.

3.0 REFERENCED DOCUMENTS

3.1 SOP 100 Rev C Validation Procedure

3.2 SOP 115 Rev F Deviation Procedure

3.3 SOP 130 Rev B Statistical Techniques Procedure

3.4 SOP 125 Rev C Document Control Procedure

3.5 SOP 127 Rev C Good Documentation Practices Procedure

3.6 Form 100 Validation Master Plan

3.7 Form 115 Deviation Form

3.8 Form 111 Attribute MSA/TMV Study Protocol

3.9 Form 112 Variable MSA/TMV Study Protocol

3.10 Form 113 MSA/TMV Report

4.0 DEFINITIONS

appraiser—The individual person making the measurements. Also referred to as the *operator.*

attribute data—Characteristic or property that is measured in terms of pass/fail or go/no-go.

bias—The difference between a measured value and a known or accepted reference value.

gage—Any device used to obtain measurements.

guard banding—The practice of utilizing the gage R&R results to reduce the range of acceptance to ensure that features are within the prescribed specifications.

linearity—Extent to which a measuring instrument's bias varies along its full operating range with the measured quantity. In a gage R&R study, linearity is the difference in the bias values throughout the expected operating range of the gage.

repeatability—The variation in measurements obtained when one measurement device is used several times by the same person to measure the same characteristic on the same product.

reproducibility—The variation in measurements made by different people using the same measuring device to measure the same characteristic on the same product.

stability—(1) Of a gage: it is the ability of a gage to retain its accuracy over time and usage; (2) of a process: a process is said to be stable if it shows no recognizable pattern of change.

variable data—Measurements that are made on a continuous scale.

5.0 RESPONSIBILITY

5.1 The quality systems manager or designee will be responsible for determining the need for the study, execution of the study, and final study report approval.

5.2 Quality engineering and manufacturing engineering are responsible for the study plan, study execution, and study report.

6.0 PROCEDURE

6.1 Test method validation numbers shall be assigned in accordance with SOP 100 Validation Procedure and recorded on Form 100 Validation Master Plan.

6.2 Determine the type of study to be conducted (Variable or Attribute). Record and close any deviations per SOP 115 Deviation Procedure and record on Form 115 Deviation Form.

6.3 To fully challenge the robustness and the ability of the measurement system, it is important to select some parts that are marginally considered good and marginally considered bad.

APPENDIX A VARIABLE R&R STUDY PROCESS AND ACCEPTANCE CRITERIA

1. Determine the number of parts, trials, and appraisers necessary to conduct the study using a risk-based approach.

2. Establish the acceptability criteria based on health and safety risk.

3. Make sure the gage has adequate discrimination.

4. Verify the calibration status of the gage.

5. Ensure that each appraiser is properly trained and has the necessary competence to perform the study.

6. Allow sufficient time for environmental stabilization of the parts and gage if applicable.

7. Collect the data and complete the two-way ANOVA data sheet.

8. Calculate the ranges of the gage R&R study.

9. Calculate the performance statistics of the R&R study.

10. Analyze the results and develop follow-up action as necessary.

11. Determine if guard banding is necessary.

12. Document the reevaluation criteria and interval.

Table G.1   Gage R&R acceptance.

Agreement	Acceptance
< 10%	Acceptable
>10%–30%	Marginally acceptable
< 30%	Unacceptable

APPENDIX B ATTRIBUTE R&R STUDY PROCESS AND ACCEPTANCE CRITERIA

1. Determine the number of parts, trials, and appraisers necessary to conduct the study using a risk-based approach.

2. Establish acceptability criteria based on risk.

3. Allow sufficient time for environmental stabilization of the parts and gage if applicable.

4. Verify the calibration status of the gage if applicable.

5. Ensure that each appraiser is properly trained and has the necessary competence to perform the study.

6. Collect the data and complete the attribute R&R study template.

7. Verify the results for each part, trial, and appraiser by circling any differences on the template.

8. Analyze the results and develop follow-up action as necessary.

9. Document the reevaluation criteria and interval.

Table G.2   Gage acceptability criteria (short form).

Agreement	Acceptance
> 90%	Acceptable
80%–90%	Marginally acceptable
< 80%	Unacceptable

Table G.3   Gage acceptability criteria with standard.

	Acceptable	Marginally acceptable	Unacceptable
Agreement	90%	80%	< 80%
False alarm rate	5%	10%	> 10%
Leak rate	2%	5%	> 5%

Table G.4   Gage acceptability criteria (Cohen's kappa statistic).

Agreement	Acceptance
> 75%	Acceptable
40%–75%	Marginally acceptable
< 40%	Unacceptable

Table G.5   Gage acceptability criteria (Fleiss's kappa statistic).

K	Interpretation
< 0	Poor agreement
0.01–0.20	Slight agreement
0.21–0.40	Fair agreement
0.41–0.60	Moderate agreement
0.61–0.80	Substantial agreement
0.81–1.00	Almost perfect agreement

Appendix H
Gage R&R Study Audit Checklist

Requirements	Compliant	Auditor notes and evidence of compliance
Do the personnel performing the study have the proper training, education, and experience?	❑ Yes ❑ No ❑ N/A	
Are adequate records of personnel performing the study's training, education, and experience maintained?	❑ Yes ❑ No ❑ N/A	
Are personnel made aware of defects and errors that may be encountered as part of their job functions?	❑ Yes ❑ No ❑ N/A	
Did the TMV result in any deviations?	❑ Yes ❑ No ❑ N/A	
Were the deviations, if any, investigated and closed?	❑ Yes ❑ No ❑ N/A	
Were some of the parts used for the study considered marginally good and bad?	❑ Yes ❑ No ❑ N/A	
Were the parts properly identified and characterized?	❑ Yes ❑ No ❑ N/A	
Were the number of parts, trials, and appraisers selected per procedure?	❑ Yes ❑ No ❑ N/A	
Are the acceptance criteria clearly defined?	❑ Yes ❑ No ❑ N/A	
Was the equipment used in the study calibrated?	❑ Yes ❑ No ❑ N/A	
Was a determination of guard banding made?	❑ Yes ❑ No ❑ N/A	
Were reevaluation criteria and interval documented?	❑ Yes ❑ No ❑ N/A	
Is the study report completed in full, with no missing data and proper GDP applied?	❑ Yes ❑ No ❑ N/A	
Are all approvals recorded in the study report?	❑ Yes ❑ No ❑ N/A	

Glossary

analysis of variance (ANOVA)—Basic statistical technique for analyzing experimental data. It subdivides the total variation of a data set into meaningful component parts associated with specific sources of variation, including interactions.

appraiser—The individual person making the measurements. Also referred to as the *operator*.

appraiser variation—The variation in the measurement system related to the appraisers.

attribute data—Characteristic or property that is measured in terms of pass/fail or go/no-go.

bias—The difference between a measured value and a known or accepted reference value.

calibration—The comparison of two instruments or measuring devices—one of which is a standard of known accuracy traceable to national standards—to detect, correlate, report, or to eliminate by adjustment any inaccuracy of the instrument or measuring device, as compared to the standard.

Cohen's kappa statistic—A statistical measure of inter-rater agreement for pass/fail or go/no-go items. Generally thought to be a more robust measure than simple percentage agreement calculation since the statistic takes into account the agreement occurring by chance.

common cause variation—Causes of variation that are inherent in a process over time. They affect every outcome of the process and everyone working in the process. *Also see* special cause variation

confidence interval—Range within which a parameter of a population (for example, mean, standard deviation, and so on) may be expected to fall, on the basis of measurement, with some specified confidence level.

confounding—Combining indistinguishably the main effect of a factor or a differential effect between factors (interactions) with the effects of other factors, block factors, or interactions in a designed experiment.

consumer's risk—Pertains to sampling and the potential risk that bad products will be accepted and shipped to the consumer.

continuous improvement (CI)—Sometimes called *continual improvement*. The ongoing improvement of products, services, or processes through incremental and breakthrough improvements.

control chart—A chart with upper and lower control limits on which values of some statistical measure for a series of samples or subgroups are plotted. The chart frequently shows a central line to help detect a trend of plotted values toward either control limit.

correlation analysis—A measure of the relationship between two data sets of variables.

correlation coefficient—Calculated value for the purpose of measuring the strength of the linear relationship between two variables.

crossed study—A study where multiple appraisers measure the same parts. This type of study is generally used when the test is nondestructive.

decision limit—The comparison of a calculated value to a critical table value used to make a statistical decision.

degrees of freedom (df)—Parameter that, in general, is the number of independent comparisons available to estimate a specific parameter and serves as a means of entering certain statistical tables. The number of unconstrained parameters in a statistical determination.

destructive measurements—Measurement, testing, and inspection of product or material that damages or destroys the product or materials so they are not usable. Contrast with *nondestructive testing*.

discrimination—Discrimination, or *resolution*, of a measurement system is its capability to detect and indicate even small changes in the measured characteristic. The main concern when selecting or analyzing a measurement system.

environmental conditions—Stated conditions under which measurements are conducted to ensure consistency.

equipment variation (EV)—The variation in the measurement system related to the measuring device or gage.

expected value—Calculated by multiplying each of the possible outcomes by the likelihood that each outcome will occur, and summing all of those values.

false alarm—When a good part is assessed as bad (producer's, type 1, or β risk).

Fleiss's kappa statistic—A statistical measure for assessing the reliability of agreement between a fixed number of raters when assigning categorical ratings to a number of items or classifying items.

F-**test**—A test using the ratios of variances for pairs of samples. Used to determine whether the populations from which two samples were taken have the same standard deviation. The *F*-distribution is usually expressed as a table of the upper limit below which *F* can be expected to lie with some confidence level for samples of a specified number of degrees of freedom.

gage—Any device used to obtain measurements.

gage accuracy—Difference between the observed average of measurements and the true average of the same parts using precision instruments (a gage).

gage linearity—Accuracy of the gage expressed throughout its entire operating range.

go/no-go—State or attribute of a unit or product. Two parameters are possible: go (conforms to specifications) and no-go (does not conform to specifications).

guard banding—The practice of utilizing the gage R&R results to reduce the range of acceptance to ensure that features are within the prescribed specifications.

in control—Description of a process where variation is consistent over time and only normal variation (common cause variation) exists.

individuals and moving range (ImR) chart. *See X* and mR (XmR) chart

interaction—In a designed experiment, a term that describes the measure of differential comparison for the responses for each version (level) of a factor at each of the several versions (levels) of one or more factors.

leak—When a bad part is assessed as good (consumer's, type 2, or α risk).

linearity—Extent to which a measuring instrument's bias varies along its full operating range with the measured quantity. In a gage R&R study, linearity is the difference in the bias values throughout the expected operating range of the gage.

lower control limit (LCL)—Control limit for points below the central line in a control chart.

lower limit of detection (LLD)—The lowest quantity of a substance that can be detected.

lower limit of quantification (LLOQ)—The value below which quantitative results may be obtained with a specified degree of confidence; the lowest concentration of an analyte that can be reliably measured.

lower specification limit (LSL)—Lower limit to which a given product or service must conform.

material review board (MRB)—Quality control committee or team, usually employed in manufacturing other materials-processing installation, that has the responsibility and authority to deal with items or materials that do not conform to fitness for use specifications.

mean square—Sum of squares divided by degrees of freedom.

measurement capability index (MCI)—A comparison of the measurement system to the feature tolerance or statistical limits. There are two common measurement capability indexes: MCI_1 and MCI_2.

measurement systems analysis (MSA)—An analysis that considers operations, procedures, devices, and other equipment or personnel used to assign a value to a characteristic being measured.

measurement uncertainty—The result of random effects and imperfect correction of systemic effects in obtaining a measurement value that results in variation from the actual true value; also known as *measurement error.*

nested study—A study where multiple appraisers measure different parts that are assumed to be homogeneous. This type of study is typically used when the test is destructive.

nominal—Desired dimension for a product feature whose size is of concern: the desired mean value for the particular dimension. The target value.

number of distinct categories—The number of categories that the measurement system can distinguish.

outlier—An observation point that is distant from other observations. Abnormal responses resulting from special causes or uncontrolled influences that occur during an experiment.

problem solving—The act of defining a problem, determining the cause of the problem, identifying, prioritizing, and selecting alternatives for a solution, and implementing a solution.

procedure—The steps in a process and how these steps are to be performed in order for the process to fulfill a customer's requirements; usually documented.

process capability—A statistical measure of the inherent process variability of a given characteristic. The most widely accepted formula for process capability is 6 sigma.

process capability index—The value of the tolerance specified for the characteristic divided by the process capability. The several types of process capability indexes include the widely used C_{pk} and C_p.

process control—The method for keeping a process within boundaries; the act of minimizing the variation of a process.

producer's risk—For a given sampling plan, refers to the probability of not accepting a lot, the quality of which has a designated numerical value representing a generally desirable level. Usually, the designated value will be the acceptable risk and quality level (AQL).

Pythagorean relationship—The relationship between the three sides of a right triangle.

range chart (*R* chart)—A control chart in which the subgroup range, *R*, evaluates the stability of the variability within a process. Control chart of the range of variation among the individual elements of a sample.

reference—In gage calibration, a standard, generally of the highest metrological quality, at a given location, from which measurements at that location are made.

regression analysis—A statistical technique for determining the best mathematical expression describing the functional relationship between one response variable and one or more independent variables.

repeatability—The variation in measurements obtained when one measurement device is used several times by the same person to measure the same characteristic on the same product.

reproducibility—The variation in measurements made by different people using the same measuring device to measure the same characteristic on the same product.

sample—One or more units of product (or a quantity of material) drawn from a lot for purposes of reaching a decision. A subset of a population.

sample size—The number of units in a sample.

special cause variation—Causes of variation that arise because of special circumstances. They are not an inherent part of a process. Special causes are also referred to as *assignable causes. Also see* common cause variation

stability—(1) Of a gage: it is the ability of a gage to retain its accuracy over time and usage; (2) of a process: a process is said to be stable if it shows no recognizable pattern of change.

stabilization—The process of environmentally conditioning the parts and the measuring device to stated conditions.

standard—The metric, specification, gage, statement, category, segment, grouping, behavior, event, or physical product sample against which the outputs of a process are compared and declared acceptable or unacceptable.

standard deviation—A computed measure of variability indicating the spread of the data set around the mean.

statistical dependence—A condition in which two random variables are not independent. The occurrence of one does affect the other.

statistical independence—A condition in which two random variables are not dependent. The occurrence of one does not affect the other.

statistically significant—The likelihood that a result or relationship is caused by something other than mere random chance.

Student's *t*-test—A method for assessing whether the means of two groups are statistically different from each other.

sum of squares—Summation of the squared deviations relative to zero, to two level means, or the grand mean of an experiment.

test method validation (TMV). *See* measurement systems analysis

tolerance—The maximum and minimum limit values a product can have and still meet customer requirements.

trials—The number of repeated measurements on the same part by the same appraiser.

type I error—An incorrect decision to reject something (such as a statistical hypothesis or a lot of products) when it is acceptable.

type II error—An incorrect decision to accept something when it is unacceptable.

upper control limit (UCL)—Control limit for points above the central line in a control chart.

upper limit of detection (ULOD)—The highest quantity of a substance that can be detected.

upper limit of quantification (ULOQ)—The value above which quantitative results may be obtained with a specified degree of confidence; the highest concentration of an analyte that can be reliably measured.

upper specification limit (USL)—Upper limit to which a given product or service must conform.

variable data—Measurements that are made on a continuous scale. Control charts based on variable data include average (*X*-bar) chart, range (*R*) chart, and sample standard deviation (*s*) chart.

variation—A change in data, characteristic, or function caused by one of four factors: special causes, common causes, tampering, or structural variation. Types of variation include time to time, part to part, within sample.

***X* and mR (*X*mR) chart**—Control chart used when working with one sample per subgroup. The moving individual samples are plotted on the *X*-bar chart rather than the subgroup range averages. The individual chart is always accompanied by a moving range chart, usually using two subgroups to calculate the moving range points.

$\bar{X}$ and *R* chart—For variable data, control charts for the averages and range of subgroups of data.

References

American Society for Quality (ASQ). Undated. "Quality Glossary." Accessed April 14, 2015. http://asq.org/glossary/a.html.

Automotive Industry Action Group (AIAG). 2002. *Measurement System Analysis*, 3rd ed. Dearborn, MI: AIAG.

Barrentine, L.B. 2003. *Concepts for R&R Studies*, 2nd ed. Milwaukee: ASQ Quality Press.

Duncan, A. J. 1986. *Quality Control and Industrial Statistics,* 4th ed. Homewood, IL: Richard D. Irwin.

Durivage, M. A. 2014. *Practical Engineering, Process, and Reliability Statistics*. Milwaukee: ASQ Quality Press.

Fleiss, J. L. 1971. "Measuring Nominal Scale Agreement among Many Raters." *Psychological Bulletin* 76 (5): 378–82.

Hicks, C. R. 1982. *Fundamental Concepts in the Design of Experiments*, 3rd ed. New York: Holt, Rinehart and Winston.

Landis, J. R., and G. G. Koch. 1977. "The Measurement of Observer Agreement for Categorical Data." *Biometrics* 33 (1): 159–74.

Mawby, W. D. 2006. *Make Your Destructive, Dynamic, and Attribute Measurement System Work for You*. Milwaukee: ASQ Quality Press.

Mehta, B. 2013. *Implementing ISO/IEC 17025:2005*. Milwaukee: ASQ Quality Press.

Pennella, C. R. 2004. *Managing the Metrology System*, 3rd ed. Milwaukee: ASQ Quality Press.

Phillips, G. CyberMetrics. http://www.cybermetrics.com/html/news/CyberMetrics_Article_Basics_of_GRR.pdf.

———. CyberMetrics. http://archive.constantcontact.com/fs002/1102564308718/archive/1110058324415.html

Siebels, D. L. 2004. *The Quality Improvement Glossary*. Milwaukee: ASQ Quality Press.

Wheeler, D. J. 2006. *EMP III: Evaluating the Measurement Process & Using Imperfect Data*. Knoxville, TN: SPC Press.

Wheeler, D. J., and D. S. Chambers. 1986. *Understanding Statistical Process Control*. Knoxville, TN: SPC Press.

Index